COME BACK WITH THE WIND

COME BACK WITH THE WIND

LES DAWSON

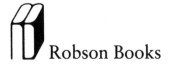

Robson Books

First published in Great Britain in 1990 by **Robson Books Ltd, Bolsover House, 5–6 Clipstone Street, London W1P 7EB**

Copyright © 1990 Les Dawson
The right of Les Dawson to be identified as author of this work has been asserted by him in accordance with the Copyright, Designs and Patents Act 1988

British Library Cataloguing in Publication Data
Dawson, Les
    Come back with the wind.
    I. Title
    823.914 [F]

    ISBN 0 86051 675 X

Typeset by Selectmove Ltd, London
Printed in Great Britain by Butler & Tanner Ltd, Frome and London

Contents

AUTHOR'S NOTE

Some of the revelations in this historical tome may well offend quite a few readers, but for that I make no apology. The story is a brutal one: of men and of women caught up in the web of conflict, finding themselves on different sides of an ideology. I've pulled no punches in describing the horrors that war provokes – the truth must be heard, or else we perish morally and revert to the savage beast. For centuries men have sought the enigma of life and the reason for our being here on this speck of cosmic dust we call Earth.

Remember the words of King Harold at the Battle of Hastings as the arrow struck home? In a tone of wonder he asked, 'Was He on our side?'

Who can forget Noah's outburst as the cataract of rain began to fall on the Ark? He turned to his wife and said simply, 'I think it's in for the day, Florrie!'

It takes a special kind of moral courage to say, as did Henry VIII to Anne Boleyn, 'Do you fancy a walk round the block?' It's that sort of thing that raises us above the animal, and we must safeguard our society against complacency.

Adversity is what we mortals thrive on. When Rathbone Mole, the classic actor, who had rehearsed for three months the words 'It is' walked on to the stage of the Old Vic on the opening night and boomed 'Is it?', he didn't flinch or lose his dignity. He merely walked proudly off the stage and said to the theatre manager, 'That proves I know the part backwards!'

I hope this account of the Civil War will make you stop in your daily activity and think deeply of the problems that had to be faced.

ACKNOWLEDGEMENTS

This novel could not have been created without the help of the following people and orgainzations:

Frisby Cotterpin's *The Lure Of Celtic Sewers*
The Sewerby Bridge Druid Society and Clark Gable Fan Club
Scott Polly's *History of Flemish Freckles*
Sheet Music by The Martha Hagget Trombone Romany Dwarf Band
The Life and Times of a Scunthorpe Missionary
A Quaker In Glossop: a study of a mole sleeping in a cupboard
Mushton Peake's *The Civil War In Ambleside and its Effect on the Gas Board*
Putting on a Surgical Boot in a Swamp: A light-hearted look at massacres
Raping Poultry by Mustapha Bird
Sanitary Conditions in Front Line Massage Parlours (University Press)
How To Cheat the Inland Revenue by prisoner number 20075

I would also like to express my sincere thanks to Professor Tailspin for his work with dead feet and also to his niece Freda for her help in going bald for charity. My thanks to Sir Oswald Comstock-Bellows for feeding an orphan in a loudspeaker during the fog in a toffee warehouse, and to all the wonderful people who sent lettuce to my grandmother whilst she was pregnant in a lighthouse. The research for this book was made that much easier by Messrs Goodfrump, Bubblebaum and Fishpaste, the Wapping solicitors who fell down a culvert whilst stapling orange peel to a ready-salted mouse. To my American publisher, 'Bugsy' Malone and his friends, many thanks for giving the wife a cement overcoat for Christmas and cutting her mother's throat.

(Dictated by Les Dawson on his secretary's knee)

GLOSSARY OF IMPORTANT
MILITARY ENGAGEMENTS

THE SIEGE
OF SANDBACH

Considered by many to be a turning point in the war, mainly due to one-way streets and a burst water main. Maintained by the Surrey Heavy Foot for a week before Easter, the siege was broken by a fleet of caravans carrying gypsy commodes to incontinent farm hands sheltering in an ear clinic. Surrender took place in a permissive launderette owned by an ex-Wren who shaved a lot.

The Northern High Command made Sandbach its headquarters, which was opened by a Mormon hairdresser and Mrs

11

Kinnock sang 'Men Of Harlech' with a jazz band.

GROPE'S FOLLY

Built in 1932 for the Pott's Belching family. The Folly, a two-storey mock-Italian castle with an outboard motor, straddled the Thames at Bray, and was of prime importance from a defence viewpoint. The Folly was stormed by the Rochdale Brigade, consisting of infantry, artillery and a man who was on holiday with his butler.

Southern troops successfully defended the stronghold against all attacks on it and the Rochdale Brigade caught a bus back to Crewe. Casualities were light and variable but it rained on the Tuesday. The Pott's Belching family capsized in a skiff and the Folly is now a museum of Norman Marital Aids and Viking whalebone vibrators for those long nights in a fiord.

MIRESEA-ON-
THE-CROUCH

Small holiday resort near the sea in Morecambe Bay. Nice walks from the minefield to the crypts where the plague victims are buried in boxes.

Nice pier with a Polish flute orchestra playing every other Wednesday. A Dutch clairvoyant gives lectures on amputations in a shed, and there's a take-away Tunisian restaurant with a lavatory that never closes. Occupied by London Marines for over a month, the Lancashire rebel government admitted to failing to capture the resort, mainly because a lot of the Lancashire troops remembered having holidays there when they were kids and paper tissues were short.

Several pitched battles took place in the area during school holidays until the lavatory fell down. Bert Barraclough, the mayor, lost his wife in the queue for the toilet; she's not dead, he's just lost her. Apparently he's not bothered, she was older than he is, and had a hare lip.

THE BATTLE
OF DELPH

Situated in the heart of Saddleworth, Delph is a small place that's rather poor – in fact the wishing well is full of IOUs. I'm not saying it used to be a bit boring, but an old colonel once looked at it and his glass eye fell asleep. It's a hilly region and the cows have longer back legs than the front so the milk doesn't spill. Southern bomber planes dropped sixteen atom bombs on it and did fifteen pounds worth of damage. Southern troops got so fed up there they surrendered before the war started. Mrs Ackroyd does cream teas there for fifty pence and she keeps frogs in a jug.

THE ATTACK ON CHESTER ZOO

Leading military experts still differ as to the tactics employed in the defence of the zoo. Some say that using orang-utans as librarians was a big mistake, but there are those who believe that dragging stuffed giraffes across a council flat helped to confuse the Southern artillery during their lunch break. Two thousand rebel troops stormed the penguin pool and a sea lion smacked an SAS bugler on the back of his knees when its striped ball stuck on his nose. Major Fitzpatrick won a VC and a packet of Players for his heroic defence of the elephant compound with

only a small bucket and shovel
against overpowering odds after
dinner.

THE BATTLE
FOR OLDHAM

Both sides looked at it; looked
again, and went to the pictures.

THE SIEGE
OF THE BBC

Northern troops charged
through the main gate at six
thirty a.m., and some were inter-
viewed on breakfast television
before the cartoons came on.
Rifle fire was heard from the
BBC canteen, but it turned out to
be a desperate attempt to soften
up the scrambled eggs. Bob
Monkhouse was taken prisoner
but was released in haste after
telling a couple of jokes with his
fixed grin.

BOLTON: THE CHARGE
OF PINFOLD'S
LIGHT HORSE

For one pound twenty, two rides
and a glass of Seven-Up. Children half-price if less than four
stone in a romper suit. Free parcels of manure if the weather's
bad, and a cork hat for fun.

Maps

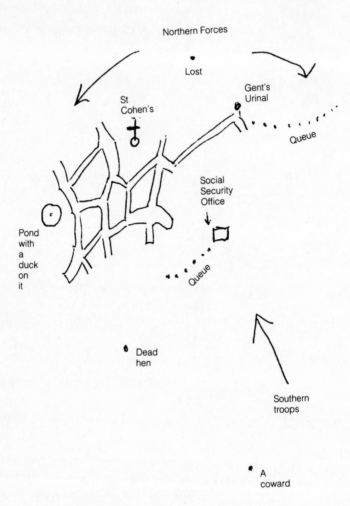

Northern Forces

Lost

Gent's
Urinal

St
Cohen's

Queue

Social
Security
Office

Pond
with
a
duck
on
it

Queue

Dead
hen

Southern
troops

A
coward

**ROUGH SKETCH OF DEFENCE
STRATEGY PRIOR TO
THE BATTLE OF COBBLER'S-ON-THE-MOUNT
(Courtesy of Florence Bott)**

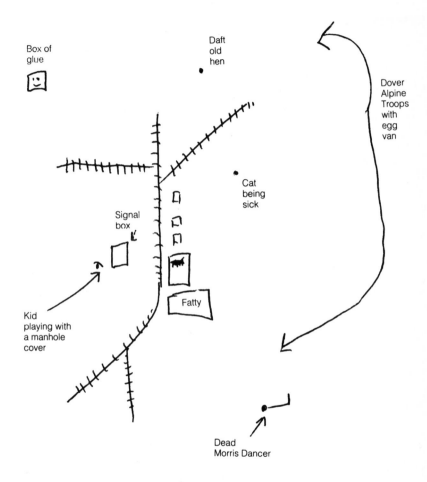

Box of glue

Daft old hen

Dover Alpine Troops with egg van

Cat being sick

Signal box

Fatty

Kid playing with a manhole cover

Dead Morris Dancer

BOGGLES CROSSING: SOUTHERN
FLANKING MOVEMENT
(Courtesy of Florence Bott)

PROLOGUE

For so very long they had regarded him as a figure of absolute ridicule but now, in the present economic climate, he had become the Messiah. They listened to his impassioned diatribes with a reverence and a respect that totally nullified the fact that, not so many months ago, his words would have brought forth jeers and abuse from the very people paying such a burning homage to him now.

He stood upon the makeshift rostrum, quivering with the fury of his oratory, and behind him gaunt grey factories severed the skyline with their dissipated profiles, shouldering tall chimneys in abandoned postures that pointed in despair to a system which discarded the men who had once fed fire into their blackened maws.

Political devastation that had laid the spirit of Man's endeavour in the dust was now the seed for civil war, sown in the rail tracks rusting into the distance. Iron lines that had once trembled under the weight of industrial merchandise were now lying dormant under a sea of creeping plant life, a choking betrayal by an indolent government.

Peabody-Brown ended his speech, and the motley crowd roared its approval for the man who preached treason and hate, violence and revolt, as a means to an end. He tasted the fruits of success and basked in the approbation so long denied him as his mindless aides, culled from the gutters, escorted him into the waiting car.

He sat back in the rear of the saloon, lit a Woodbine cigarette and bared his teeth in a vulpine grin. He savoured his moment of triumph and waved a non-chalant hand to the huddled groups who lined the grimy streets to watch his departure. Peabody-Brown drew immense satisfaction from the knowledge that his speech today would be swiftly echoed from the depressed ghettos of Tyneside and Glasgow to the silent docks of Liverpool and Hull. Not bad, he mused, considering his background; it had certainly not been one to give the impression of future greatness . . .

John Peabody-Brown squirmed into the world from his mother's innards and, after taking one look at him, his father ran away from home and changed his appearance. His mother offered to sell him to a nurse with connections in the Middle East, then pretended that she had an extended attack of amnesia. The young Brown was rather awful to look at, and well-meaning friends of the family put shutters on his pram.

Mrs Brown slept with a lot of chaps over the years, and if any one of the blades attempted to avoid paying her for services rendered 'twixt the sheets, she had only to hold John Peabody aloft in the nude to make the lout give forth what he owed.

Little John rarely left the sanctuary of his mother's council maisonette, for on one occasion Mrs Brown had put the wee thing naked upside down in his trolley, and passers-by thought the lad had lumps under his nose and a cleft chin. After that incident, she bought him a cap and let him see the world through the lounge window.

The young John Peabody was not a bright student and his teacher made him stand in the corner of the classroom so often that the lad grew a triangular forehead, which many pupils thought was a distinct improvement. During his formative years, he was in a class by himself . . . he smelt. He had no friends and indulged in competitive self-abuse behind trees. As a small boy he would corner a little girl in the quadrangle and say, 'Give me a kiss or a penny.' By the time he was fourteen he had enough to buy an Aston Martin. He was so ugly, if he went to see a horror film at the local cinema, the audience thought he was making a personal appearance. He grew up angry in a world that was already angry. England north of Birmingham was dying both culturally and industrially. Geordies and Scousers worked as slave labour in wealthy Southern homes and woe betide any spirited Northern lad who made a pass at a Southern Belle.

The opiate of real ale and fish and chips kept the North in a subservient mood, and the government introduced a system of tax cuts for Morris Dancers and free meals for whippets. They were desperate times, but the North lacked a leader to harness that tragic despair into a coherent demand for justice . . . Only half-wits harangued the masses.

At first Peabody-Brown (he gave himself a hyphen as a cheap free gift) stood on street corners passing out political leaflets to pedestrians; then he moved on to a heckling squad whose job it was to boo and interrupt speakers at meetings. Three times he was arrested and he served a total of nine months imprisonment – not for political agitating, but for urinating up a policeman's tunic.

In rapid succession, Peabody-Brown joined the 'Oswald Mosley Men of Winsford' movement, then the 'Bomb Watford Gap', an idiot group from an open prison in Kirkham; just as rapidly, he was dropped like a hot potato from the two factions after streaking through a museum in Stafford. But as conditions worsened in the North, his voice would not be stilled and people began to heed his barmy words despite themselves. The North became denuded of its young men and women as they trekked south in search of work, and 'Grab A Granny Nights' were introduced into discos.

Peabody-Brown's following grew, and not even the interview in a popular newspaper in which his mother stated that her son hadn't the intelligence of a geranium, could stem the tide of opinion that was turning in his favour. Thus are the seeds of destiny germinated by a fickle sort of galactic roulette. Ere long, questions began to be asked in the House of Commons about the dubious Mr Peabody-Brown and his role in the growing crisis, and the Member for Purley East went as far as to hire a sleuth from Dartford to follow Brown about in case he turned out to be a poof.

Europe looked askance at the goings-on in Britain, and Bangladesh had the gall to send Liverpool some food parcels. It became a common sight to see child beggars in the streets of Northern towns and tourists in the Lake District were hounded and, in some reported cases, attacked by teenagers for money needed to play 'Space Invaders'.

Thus it was that John Peabody-Brown emerged as the Hope for Northern Britain as the clamour for national division grew into fury and hatred.

Pen sketch of the legendary 'Hairy Mildred' who scattered a platoon of Southern troops in Darlington by yodelling a Jewish country and western song and setting fire to snuff.
(*Sketch courtesy of 'The Addled Collection', Ramsbottom*)

THE BEGINNING

'We have the will and we will see that
will through. We will succeed with having
that will, and that will never let us down.
Will we? Of course we will, the will is
there, and it will be done.'
                    (Extract from a speech by Florence Bott)

The party on the lawn that yawned away from the large
mock-Tudor house was a riot of summer dresses and
bright laughter. Ardent young men flirted madly with
the flushed nubile girls who paraded their charms in coy
competition, the muted strains of a Lionel Ritchie ballad
joined in a descant with the clink of champagne glasses
and behind a thicket a cat was sick.

Mrs Emily O'Mara sat fanning herself under the
willow tree and watched the knot of eligible males
hovering around the hammock where her lovely wild
daughter, Carla, sat holding court to the burning swains.
Mrs O'Mara sighed with a deep satisfaction; life was so

good here in Henley-on-Thames . . . The beautiful house
built by her husband, an ex-bricklayer from Cork who
had made his fortune from manufacturing do-it-yourself
kitchen units and glazed bidets; the lazy Thames that
brushed the edge of the well-manicured gardens; and
the O'Mara five-berth speed-launch bobbing gently at its
moorings . . . she sighed again in utter contentment. She
had all that, and a wonderful daughter to dote upon.

Carla O'Mara, was without doubt, the most adorable
of all God's creatures. The cascade of flame-red curly
hair complemented perfectly the large green eyes and
fulsome lips that could quiver with happiness or pout
with anger. The girl's figure was divine and every man
who met her fell under the spell of her beauty . . . Carla
O'Mara was the envy of every other maiden and, for one
of her kisses, a young man would have gladly gone forth
to blaze a trail in Uganda or to open an account with
American Express.

One disappointed suitor had fled England after being
rejected by Carla, and was now a humble penitent in
a religious order in the Sudan. Others had joined the
French Foreign Legion, and at least one young man had
been eaten by somebody in Borneo. Carla had merely to
lift her dainty finger and men swooned for her favours.

Except one – Ashton Whelks, a dreamy slim poet
with slight acne, who worked in a library. He seemed
indifferent to Miss O'Mara's charms, and that was the
only cloud in Carla's life. She sat on the hammock, bored
now by the attention, and suddenly her eyes narrowed as
she espied Ashton, morris dancing with her close friend
Melanie. 'Damn her,' Carla thought, her gaze riveted on
the young man's stockings with the ribbons flying as he
pranced and waved his stick.

She returned to the present with a start and drank deeply from her glass. 'Why, bless my soul, George,' she said to a lovelorn teenager who was trying to peer down her frock, 'I do declare you want to ravish me.' Amid the peal of laughter at the expense of the blushing youth, she kicked him smartly in the crutch and he doubled up in agony.

If the house party on the lawn was a carousel of gaiety, the older guests in the vast book-lined O'Mara study seemed oblivious to it. There was an air of solemnity draping the prosperous gathering of bankers and politicians and the conversation was one of speculative foreboding. Despite the mood, however, O'Mara senior, holding forth beneath a portrait of his late father who had been sucked down in a bog after being chewed by an Army mule, looked at his guests with pride. Not bad, he thought, for a bricklayer – two high-ranking clerics, three important politicians and the Under Secretary for Foreign Affairs, not to mention the Prime Minister's advisor on finances.

There was so much power in that room: men who held high station, men who manipulated great companies with ruthless efficiency, and men who were determined to safeguard their preserves from the threats of any society. The purse-strings of a nation were held in the hands of a few, and all were intimate colleagues of the O'Mara family.

'Something has to be done about that damned fellow. What's his name? Oh, yes, Peabody-Brown. The man's an idiot.' This was grunted by a large-girthed gentleman from Bagshot who did things in Whitehall and had difficulty in passing water. The name 'Peabody-Brown' threw the assembly into a state of anger, and bitter words were exchanged. One man, standing by the window, looking out at the merry scenes on the lawns, said nothing. He simply smiled a tight smile and listened to the outbursts around him. Finally, as the uproar died down, he strode to the middle of the room and his very presence invited a respectful silence. He had a magnetic quality and a most commanding figure. Tall, well over six feet, with broad shoulders and dark good looks, he did not appear to be the sort of man to trifle with. A thin moustache gave his lips a broad line and brought attention to a firm, wide chin. His clothes were impeccably tailored and yet there was an air of coarseness about him, a raffish attitude that tended to make people feel uneasy in his company.

O'Mara stood by the stranger's side and said, loudly: 'Gentlemen, I think it's time we heard the views of my friend here. He had just returned from the North and knows more than we do about the state of the thinking up there.'

The tall man nodded to O'Mara and, taking the expensive cigar from his mouth, he spoke in a rasping tone. The men around stood in anticipation. 'Gentlemen, you talk of one Peabody-Brown. A firebrand, yes, an idiot, maybe, but gentlemen, he has the ear of the North.' He paused and sipped his brandy. 'For years in the South, you have allowed the economic conditions of the industrial North to go unchecked. Promises were made and broken. In a country as small as ours, it is inconceivable that so little is known about the Northern way of life to anybody living south of Watford Gap. Gentlemen, England is a nation divided.' His words brought forth an outburst of protest but, with a wave of his strong hands, he silenced them, and his matter-of-fact analysis riveted his audience.

He informed them about the threatened embargo on whisky sales to the South. This news brought gasps of horror from a middle-aged vicar, and an elderly banker had to hold on to the table as he heard it. The powerful men heard about the proposal to build a series of Customs and Excise sheds along the Staffordshire border with Cheshire. Mutely they heard about the new-forged friendship between Lancashire and Yorkshire; in disbelief, they listened to the information that Yorkshire cricketers had been given a ticker-tape welcome at Old Trafford. Their faces now drained of blood, they heard how the Red Rose of Lancaster and the White Rose of York had been scrapped in favour of a blue-tinged tulip. In his unemotional voice, the tall stranger painted a picture of untold horrors: of how Brown Windsor soup was banned from school dinners, of how Moslem children in Bradford were being taught that jellied eels could give them Aids or, at best, prolonged dysentery.

The Southern moguls reeled under the realization that the North was planning to break away from the rest of Britain, to become a separate state, self-governing under this man, Peabody-Brown, who wore a suit of Lincoln green in honour of Robin Hood and who was now the emblem of the struggle for freedom.

'. . . And so, gentlemen, don't make the mistake of treating this business too lightly,' the stranger said, as Lord Delamere threw up in a vase. 'They mean to press ahead with their plans to partition the country.' Heavy breathing followed the stranger's summary, and old Sir

Willoughby Willoughby muttered: 'Would it help things if we gave 'em a few bob towards a motorway?' In an effort to lighten the atmosphere, O'Mara suggested that they should join the main party on the lawn and the elders commenced to shuffle out of the study.

Carla rose from the hammock, aware of the tall dark man looking at her with undisguised hunger. She sniffed and tossed her curls in disdain, but the stranger merely seemed amused at her gesture. Angrily, she went in search of Ashton Whelks, but she hadn't got further than the summerhouse when her father beckoned her over to where he sat, with the tall dark man she had just cut dead.

'Carla,' her father said, 'Let me introduce you to an acquaintance of mine, Mr Albert Butler.'

White teeth flashed as the man bowed his head and her heart thumped like an over-stretched drumskin. 'Pleased to meet you, Miss O'Mara,' he rasped.

Carla curtsied. 'Likewise, I'm sure, Mr Butler.'

He smiled again. 'Not Mr Butler, I beg of you . . . Call me by my nickname: Red.'

His eyes devoured her beauty and she felt as if he had stripped her to her vest and knickers with his piercing gaze. She coloured and ran away behind the gazebo. Then she wished she hadn't. For, behind a potted fern inside the summerhouse, she saw Ashton Whelks in an embrace with Melanie. Carla's eyes swam with tears; her whole body shook with jealousy and rage and it took an effort of will to stop herself marching into the gazebo and pulling Melanie's hair out by its roots.

She balled her hands into tight fists as she clearly heard Whelks say, in a trembling voice, 'Love you, Melanie my darling.'

'You shall not have him, you insipid bitch!' Carla grated through her teeth and with that she sidled away through the shrubbery, oblivious to the cat being sick in it.

The party seemed to be breaking up and making for the house. Curious, Carla followed the guests into the elegant lounge, and sullenly wondered why they seemed to be grouping around the television screen.

The early evening news flickered into focus and she saw her father and his influential friends listening avidly to the newsreader. '. . . The demonstration was broken up by the police, but it is feared that the Prime Minister was hit several times with a panful of Lancashire hot-pot as he walked into the Guildhall.' The newsreader paused, and there appeared on the screen a rather large lady in a red hat, smacking the Prime Minister's head with a saucepan. The contents of the vessel could be seen dribbling down the Prime Minister's waistcoat from a mound of stew in the middle of his bald head.

'. . . Several people have been arrested at a football match in London after Manchester United supporters tried to hang the referee when their team lost three–nil to Chelsea. I've just been handed a news flash.' The newscaster cleared his throat. 'John Peabody-Brown, the self-appointed Prime Minister for the North of England, has stated that Lancashire and Yorkshire, with Cumbria and Northumberland, have declared that they are no longer to be governed by Westminster, and that all Southern-based companies in the North are to be taken over by the new Confederation of Counties. Mr Peabody-Brown spoke earlier today in Halifax.' The screen shimmered for a moment, and then on came a picture of Peabody-Brown in his suit of Lincoln green,

addressing a packed hall in the town. O'Mara's guests
watched in a stunned silence as they viewed the waving
banners and the neo-Nazi uniforms of the mass listening
to their leader.

'Fellow Northerners, the time is approaching for all
true men of this great shire to stand and be counted.
For years we have been been enslaved by the faceless
politicians of Westminster; our cotton mills now lie
empty and dead, our coal mines defunct and our shipyards closed . . . Our children are without bread, our
womenfolk in rags.' He paused and shook his bow and
arrow, and his face was screwed into a grimace of rage.
'The South have all the economic wealth and the good
life is theirs at our expense; our sweat; our blood. Well,
enough is enough my friends, and I call on Cheshire and
aye, Birmingham, to rally to the flag of rebellion . . . This
flag, the flag of Freedom!'

At that point, two burly men in peaked caps joined
Peabody-Brown on the rostrum and unfurled a standard
upon which was a Yorkshire Pudding and a Lancashire
Black Pudding on a background of chipped potatoes.

O'Mara's powerful clique stood rooted to the spot as
the news ended and the screen went blank. 'My God,'
declared Sir Noel Potts, 'it's worse than I thought.'
Lord Minehead sneered, in a withering tone, 'The
lunatic should be be damn well horsewhipped,' and
the Archdeacon announced it was the time of the Anti-
Christ, then fell asleep on the sofa.

Carla pouted. Her party was in ruins. 'Fiddlesticks.'
she brayed. ''Tis only a storm in a teacup.' And
with that she tried to entertain the gathering with
a spirited tap-dance and an impression of Jimmy
Cagney.

Red Butler stood alone in the corner of the room with a sardonic smile on his lips . . . Storm in a teacup, eh? How little they knew, these fat sleek idiots. War was in the air but they were too blind to see it. Red Butler shrugged his shoulders. He would do all right out of the coming conflict; already he was making an enormous profit from smuggling whisky into the South. His main concern now was how to get Carla O'Mara's knickers down.

To prevent the guests from leaving in despondency, Carla tried juggling with lemons at the front door. But the television news had driven any gaiety there might have been firmly away.

Hordes of reporters besieged 10 Downing Street as the Prime Minister hurried from his car, still wiping the hot-pot from his clothing. 'Stupid bloody old fart,' the PM thought to himself, still seething at the woman who had hit him with the pan. The fact that she was in custody didn't appease him in the slightest. 'I'd like to wring her bloody neck,' he muttered to himself.

His inner councillors were awaiting him in the drawing-room. They had been hastily summoned after the Peabody-Brown broadcast, and the grim lines on their faces gave mute evidence of the seriousness of the situation.

All reports were closely studied and a definite picture was emerging. All citizens who had been born south of Watford, but who had settled in the North, were being turned out of their homes and sent packing, back to where they had come from. Those who defied the deportation order were no longer allowed to drink

Newcastle Brown in the pubs, and the singing of 'Maybe It's Because I'm A Londoner' was regarded as an act of treason.

American tourists at Heathrow had been hi-jacked and flown to Blackpool for a fortnight's holiday, and all Asian immigrants had to learn to say, 'Eeh Bah Gum.' Fish from Fleetwood was no longer to be found in the Home Counties and there wasn't a decent rissole to be had in the West End. But what to do? That was the dilemma in front of the Council. Her Majesty the Queen had made it plain that her affections lay in Balmoral, and the Duke of Edinburgh had openly stated that he personally wouldn't mind a place in the Isle of Man.

The Prime Minister banged the table with his gavel. 'Gentlemen, we have to do something . . . discredit this imbecile Peabody-Brown, or have him shot or whatever. Any ideas?' he asked wistfully.

Field Marshal Harcourt-Lee blew his nose and rumbled, 'Invasion,' and went out to the lavatory.

The PM glared around at the Council. 'Well, what the hell do we do?' Nobody spoke up. 'Bloody marvellous, isn't it?' the PM yelled. 'Scotland and the North openly telling us to get stuffed, and not one of you can think of a damn thing to do.'

The Prime Minister's close confidant, Mallory Price-Carpenter, rose to his expensively shod feet, tapped his dentures with a pencil, and then commenced to stride around the room.

The Prime Minister glared at Price-Carpenter, and with good reason: Price-Carpenter only hung on to his job because he had the negatives of some photographs taken at a party where the PM had been found in bed with a set of blonde twins and a rhino whip. 'We have to tread with great caution,' said Price-Carpenter. 'The Americans will make tremendous capital out of it all should we make the wrong decision, and we'll probably finish up as a suburb of Detroit.'

Suddenly, the oak-panelled doors were flung ajar, and in charged the Leader of the Opposition, Fred Hardcastle. An odd-looking man with an obvious hernia, Hardcastle had been a miner and a merchant seaman before opening a massage parlour in Durham. He was a forceful politician and yearned for a knighthood. Many people feared him, some sneered at him, and his wife was having it away with a coloured draughtsman.

Hardcastle's nostrils were flared in anger and he thumped the table in a white fury. 'What the hell is going on? The bloody country is on the verge of a civil war, and no bugger tells me what's going on.' He paused to regain his breath and the PM took the opportunity to defuse the situation. Of course the Opposition Leader should have been informed, but the man was such a cretin . . .

'My dear chap, several times messages have been sent to you; even two of them via 3 Bellamy Street.' The PM pursed his lips, as the impact of his last few words sank home – 3 Bellamy Street was the home of an ex-Cossack who catered for any male sexual fantasy. On his books the ex-Cossack had a Druid who liked to be called an elf whilst being hit on his bare behind with a spiked frankfurter, two stockbrokers who enjoyed tap-dancing on the stomach of a chimpanzee, and a rather gloomy Baron whose sole satisfaction in life was to throw horse dung up a Scotsman's kilt.

The PM knew he'd have no further trouble from Hardcastle. The mere mention of 3 Bellamy Street had destroyed the Labour leader's carefully planned oral attack on the PM. Despite a positive blanket of secrecy in left-wing corridors of power, most people knew that Hardcastle was a bit peculiar when it came to good old hanky-panky. Nobody really knew what switched Hardcastle on, but the ex-Cossack kept a Malay duck in black suspenders in the cellar with an ostrich that buried its head in a bucket of condoms. Hardcastle would spend hours in the cellar playing a piano accordion in the nude and calling the duck 'Mother.'

After the PMs mention of 'Bellamy Street' the Opposition leader stormed out in a towering state of frustration and rage, and the Inner Council resumed its task of sifting the evidence in an effort to grasp the enormity of the political crisis.

What emerged was indeed a most harrowing picture of ineptitude and governmental bungling intermingled with absolute ignorance of events, both social and economic.

Southerners thought that the average Northerner was a beery ne'er-do-well who wore a flat cap and carried a whippet around in a brown paper bag. They thought Northern men were bone-idle Communists who clouted their womenfolk with lengths of tripe and fed their kids on chips and mushy peas.

On the other hand, the Northerner, bless him, was fully convinced that anybody who lived south of Watford was a pompous poof in a bowler hat who drank beer that was so weak no one ever got drunk on it, but just suffered from an attack of the bends. The Northern attitude was still steeped in the tradition of the depressed Thirties: the North made the brass, London spent it. Frankly, over the years, there had been some justification for that mental approach. Successive governments had shied away from the problem of industrial changes and had seemed to be content to take the Mr Micawber view of 'Something Will Turn Up' . . . and of course it hadn't.

The introduction of shipyard containers into Liverpool meant that the dockers could no longer steal things from the ships, and that perk was a part of the great port's historic past. So the stunned Liverpudlians went into successive strikes, and many went peculiar and started to support Everton.

Southern businessmen didn't fancy pouring money into the North-East of England and so, for instance, Jarrow decayed as a ship-building area and nobody offered to invest in any diverse industry. Thus was a wasteland born. West Hartlepool made a valiant effort to lure several companies up into the town, but as the inhabitants had once hung a monkey there in the belief that it was a Frenchman it didn't seem a good idea at the time.

Meanwhile, the South prospered, and Stringfellows was doing well, and in the House of Commons some old fool from Bromley West suggested selling the North of England to Pontin's. Naturally, in absurd times such as these, the stage was set for the debut of an idiot like Peabody-Brown.

When he was thirty-five years of age, Peabody-Brown's mother left him on a launderette doorstep whilst she got a job with a blacksmith. Her job was simple enough: when the shoes were ready, she handed him the horse. Her son was very annoyed with his mother's

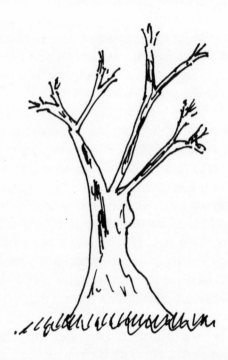

'Arkwright's Tree' used extensively by London Cavalry as a horse urinal and a place for staff dances. The Southern invasion of Yorkshire was halted here by Bert Wormold and his wife Elsie who ran a mobile bingo stall. The advance resumed after a full house was won by a corporal who spent his winnings on a tattoo. (*Sketch drawn by a nude pacifist*)

high-handed attitude and wrote to his father, who was in a Queensland jail for fraud. At the termination of his sentence, Peabody-Brown senior and his son were reunited in a caravan and both hoped to win on the football coupon.

Peabody-Brown never lost the hope that his mother would one day call back to the launderette and claim him, because it was getting colder by the minute and he wasn't sleeping all that well on the doorstep. His mother, as well as working for the blacksmith, also appeared on the stages of various working-men's clubs in a trampoline act and worked part time as a decoy for a sex shop.

He sent her many letters, all of them written by hand, but he never got a reply from her until he started writing them with a pen. His mother was deeply moved by the correspondence, and made up her mind to be reunited with her son and heir. She gave the blacksmith a week's notice and he was sorry to see her go; he'd enjoyed her company, and found her most agreeable, especially when she bent over the anvil.

Mr Brown senior, in an effort to stop smoking, took to eating raw vegetables and became totally hooked on carrots; he was an addict but found that he could see better.

Peabody-Brown's mother had a heart attack whilst arm-wrestling, and passed away in a pool of spilt Britvic and crushed nuts on the pub floor. Peabody-Brown's father never got over her death and he was finally taken away in an unlettered van with a parcel of carrots to a big house on a hill. His son visited him a few times, but his father thought he was a rabbit after his carrots on one visit, and hit his son with a spin-dryer.

At the age of thirty-six, John Peabody-Brown was alone in the world, except for an aunt who was a lesbian with the coal board. He couldn't get a job anywhere. Later, it was said that one of his insurance stamps was worth more than a Penny Black. He became bitter and morose and took to reading books on Lenin and Karl Marx, although he admitted in later life that he had always liked *Fanny Hill* better.

On a rare visit to London, he underwent an experience that was to fan the flames of a burning hatred for the South. More by accident than design, he wandered into the Savoy Hotel and seated himself at a table in the elegant dining room. Sullenly he ordered the soup of the day from a haughty waiter.

Abruptly, the reverent silence in the dining room was broken by Peabody-Brown's thick accent: 'Cum 'ere you,' he said to the aloof waiter. 'Cum 'ere, I can't eat this soup.' This was too much for the *maître d'hôtel*, who had been watching Peabody-Brown with mounting horror. He gestured to the waiter that he himself would attend to the ill-kempt dreadful little man.

'What seems to be amiss . . . sir?' The word 'sir' was spat from sneering lips. Peabody-Brown looked up at the superbly draped figure of the *maître d'hôtel*, and self-consciously blurted out: 'I can't eat this bloody soup.'

The *maître d'hôtel* snapped: 'How dare you say you cannot eat the soup! Our chef, the divine Enrico, is renowned for his exquisite soups, not to mention his fricassee of musk ox. At this very table, crowned heads of Europe have drooled in a positive ecstasy over his *jambon chaud à la chablisienne 'Alexandre Dumain'*. Enrico is a god in the orbit of the culinary arts. Famous stage and film stars have sat at this table and waxed eulogies over the cuisine. This dining room is a hallowed sanctum for the gourmet; a Valhalla for the discerning. Now, you product of a Northern slum, you have the audacity to squat in your cheap fustian and have the gall to say that you cannot eat the soup. Before I have you pitchforked into the gutter from where you no doubt came, I will ask you only once: why cannot you eat the soup?'

Peabody-Brown replied 'I haven't got a spoon.'

From that moment on, Peabody-Brown vowed that one day he'd turn the Savoy into a waffle bar and that London as an international metropolis would cease to exist and become a general sort of open-air museum with sound Yorkshire management.

He threw himself into the turbulent cauldron of extreme political ideologies; he called out Bingo numbers for the National Front; tried to infiltrate the IRA, posing as a lame Mormon transvestite, until he got involved in a gang bang in Belfast – he limped for some time after that. He attempted to stand as a left-wing Liberal, but the Liberals wouldn't stand for him; in a fit of depression, he became a Fascist but his black shirt got lost in a bus depot. Finally, he found his forte in the unrest of the Northern economic collapse and, at last, Peabody-Brown had come into his own. He was the leader of the revolutionary party: The Anarchist Right Wing Left of Centre Workers' Union. In the beginning there was only himself, an elderly orphan, and two reformed muggers in the movement, but after a successful raid on a Notting Hill Gate toilet, where posters were stuck on the walls that extolled the virtues of his party, more eccentrics were drawn to Peabody-Brown's ideals and they started to become a damn nuisance.

In the Fulham Road, Peabody-Brown's barmy brigade glued leaflets on the backs of passers-by; they let stink bombs off in Carnaby Street and the smell gave a Korean tourist a mild attack of angina. In Park Lane, a pair of

Wigan dancing clogs were thrown into the Dorchester Hotel and, at the point of a horse pistol, a commercial radio station disc jockey was forced to play a record of 'On Ilkley Moor Ba't 'At' for over three hours. As unemployment grew in the North, so the ranks of Peabody's supporters began to swell into hundreds and, in a fiery speech in the House of Commons, a Northern MP hurled his truss at Black Rod.

Despite the drama being unfolded, life for Carla O'Mara was a frivolous carousel of parties and gaiety; she was the centre of attraction in high society, but she still yearned for the arms of Ashton Whelks around her. He, on the other hand, had only eyes for his beloved Melanie, and Carla hated her more and more each day.

Red Butler came to the O'Mara house many times with stolen consignments of whisky, but Carla ignored his blandishments and beat him once at snooker. Melanie, having no idea of Carla's true feelings for her, continued to confide her growing love for Whelks and she dropped a bombshell one late afternoon as they were both sipping mint tea on the lawns of the O'Mara mansion which bore the simple name of Tara. The house had been named after a relative in Ireland who constantly sang; 'Ta-ra-ra-boom-de-ay' when drunk; he'd finally got on people's nerves and had been tarred and feathered in a convent.

'Dear, dear Carla,' crooned Melanie that warm afternoon, 'I am so very happy, sweet friend. Ashton has asked my papa for my hand in marriage. We are unofficially engaged.' Carla felt faint, and it was if someone had struck her a blow. Melanie and Ashton?

NO, *no, no* ... Outwardly she forced a a smile, but inwardly she longed to put her hands around Melanie's throat and squeeze the life out of her simpering body.

'Why, Ashton?' she asked herself. 'Melanie hasn't my beauty, nor does she possess the furnace of a burning sensuality that drives me insane for you ... Oh, Ashton my love, why are you so blind?' The instant she conjured up that last unspoken thought, she regretted it, for Ashton Whelks did have defective vision. In fact he was so short-sighted, he wore Braille socks.

Carla's bitter ruminations were broken by the sound of Melanie's sweet voice: 'Carla, darling, are you not feeling well?'

Carla pulled herself back to the present and, with a toss of her red tresses, replied impatiently, 'Why fiddle-de-de, Melanie, of course I'm all right.' She spoke brightly, not wanting Melanie to know how she ached inside.

The two women sat in a companionable silence, watching birds flying over the Thames that shimmered under the heat of a benign sun. Melanie sipped her mint tea as she clutched her bundle of Ashton Whelks' love letters in her right hand, and Carla unfastened her bra and took out a hip flask and drank the vodka from it neat. From the library window, Carla's mother smiled and broke wind.

In a sound-proof room, somewhere in Whitehall, the Prime Minister, along with high-ranking Army personnel, poured over maps of strategic areas of England; they pored over the problems they would have to face if the decision was made to invade the North.

In a discreetly situated club in the heart of the Black Country, distinguished members of the Birmingham Council voted unanimously to keep the Midlands neutral in the face of the coming Civil War and, having made that momentous landmark in history, they finished off their faggots and peas and watched the stripper.

In Manchester, several small tailoring businesses were given orders for the uniforms that would be worn by the Northern Army. Flat, long-peaked caps with crossed brass clogs at the front and a woollen black pudding hanging from the back. Grey trousers and double-breasted grey jackets (with large pockets for sandwiches and light ales) and stout black boots made up the ensemble agreed upon for all the conscripts; the only marked difference would be that the Scottish regiments would wear, instead of the trousers, polythene kilts to avoid them getting chapped legs.

In Cardiff, the Welsh ruling junta decided to break away from everybody and ask for a Common Market grant in order to increase their male-voice choirs. The only Welshmen allowed to speak English, it was decreed, would be Rugby Union players so that they could swear at Continental referees.

*

Northern Ireland voted against sending troops to help the Peabody-Brown Government, but promised to send plenty of draught Guinness and comedians to assist the Cause.

Despite the pleas from churches of all denominations, the die was cast for war and, in the South, any clergyman born north of Watford Gap was unfrocked and forced to work on the M25 to cover up all the cracks. The North retaliated by handcuffing Southern-born priests and vicars together and making them sit through six episodes at a time of 'EastEnders'. This type of physical ordeal was frowned on by the Geneva Convention and so, reluctantly, Peabody-Brown had to drop the soap opera and substitute Bugs Bunny and Postman Pat.

America watched with anxious eyes at the developing tragedy and a specialist told the President that, if he attempted to dye his hair any more, it would turn technicolour.

The Russians remained passive and watchful; they had enough troubles of their own. The Chinese had opened a chain of take-aways in Moscow and half the adult population was now hooked on chow mein and rice wine and the vodka industry was in a desperate plight. Six successive Five-Year Plans had failed and the Bolshoi Ballet had grown out of their tights.

Meanwhile, back in Whitehall, a plan was hatched to infiltrate the Birmingham area. Secretly, by night, Southern troops were to be dropped by parachute on the M6; they would take command of Fort Dunlop and use the tyre company's depot as a sort of brick Gibraltar to halt any military moves from the North to the South.

Parliament bribed Birmingham Council with a promise
to subsidize the motor car industry and repaint the Bull
Ring.

What the Prime Minister had overlooked was that one
of his Generals, Sir Caspar Merrypepper, had an auntie
who lived in Fleetwood and she demanded loyalty to the
Northern cause from her nephew or else she would cut
him out of her will and tell the press about his boyfriend
in Malta. And so General Merrypepper became a double
agent in order to get his aunt's cash and send flowers to
Carlos in Valetta.

Merrypepper's note informing him of the proposed
military takeover of Fort Dunlop galvanized Peabody-
Brown into action. 'The time is now,' he crowed to
his inner council, and immediately bought a round of
drinks and a packet of cheese-flavoured crisps. By this
time, in the eddy of events, all football matches between
Northern teams and the South had been abandoned after
an ugly incident during a game between Manchester City
and West Ham. Three players from the London-based
team had sneaked into Manchester City's changing
rooms before the match and deliberately sprayed Algipan
in the Northern lads' jock-straps. This created agonized
whoops in the goal-mouth, and a penalty kick was ruined
when a Manchester City player, clawing at his reddened
buttocks, booted the ball and his shorts fell down. The
ball went into the stands and smacked the chin of a
Jehovah's Witness who thought an atheist had hit him
– the only thing that could calm him down was a pound
for the collection plate and a promise of a photograph of
Samantha Fox in a pair of gold lamé boots.

All military personnel born of Southern stock were
sent back from Northern garrisons to a hastily-erected

transit camp near Sandbach, where they were refitted into Southern uniforms of blue denim trousers, red Homburg hats and white capes. From there, they were transported to Aldershot for a debriefing session and grilled turbot.

The country was now divided.

The good life had now soured for Carla O'Mara. The unfolding drama around her meant nothing to the spoilt wilful beauty. Only one thing mattered to her, the conquest of Ashton Whelks. The parties at Tara had lost their zest; the young ardent swains who had once lain prostrate at her size fours had eagerly joined the Southern Army and her circle of girlfriends kept diminishing as the belles enlisted in the nursing services. Such was the fever of patriotism that even Ashton Whelks attempted to get into the Army; but his eyes were so bad he tripped over a cow on his way to a medical examination at a cottage hospital.

Carla lay in wait one night in her E-type Jaguar for Ashton Whelks to return from a lecture at the village hall on the mating habits of the Malay Fruit Bat, and she gripped the steering wheel tightly as she espied Ashton leaving the hall. Tonight she was going to seduce him away from that wretched creature Melanie and claim him as her very own.

She clambered out of the sports car and cried; 'Ashton! Over here.' She saw him peer around and start talking to a wall. 'No, dearest, I'm over here,' she said petulantly and ran across to lead him to her car. They drove off in silence; she racked her brains for a memory of a secluded place wherein she could undertake the

seduction. Whelks remained nervously toying with his
pipe. Finally, after burning his nose on a match whilst
trying to light his battered briar, Whelks blurted out:
'Where are we going, Carla? I must get back to Melanie,
she's invited some people over for Scrabble.'

She didn't answer him. Instead, spotting a rut that led
through a tangled copse, she swung the wheel over and
the small car bounced into a thicket where a cat was
being sick again.

There was no time for talk of romance: Action was
what was required. Carla braked the vehicle, switched
off the engine and threw her arms round Whelk's thin
shoulders. Passion mounted between them; they writhed
and caressed madly, and Carla unfastened the zip on his
flyhole.

Despite his reluctance, Whelks found himself returning
the heat of her ardour, and before long they were both
naked and struggling for a foothold in the confined space
of the E-type. Whelks moaned as he massaged Carla's
silky rump . . .

'Oh, darling Ashton,' she crooned, 'I'll have to change
my position. I've got cramp.' The agony of her frozen leg
muscle caused her to heave Ashton over to the central
area of the car. Whelks suddenly bellowed loudly, like
a stricken moose.

'Oh, Ashton,' Carla panted, 'are you having an or-
gasm, my love?'

As a reply, Whelks shook his head as tears came to his
weak eyes.

'No, no. Oh, Carla,' he brayed painfully, 'help me,
please! The gearstick . . . get me off the gearstick.'

Carla, now thoroughly alarmed, switched the interior
light on and gasped in horror at what she saw: the

gearstick was imbedded in Ashton's rectum. Hastily putting on her drawers, she climbed out of the car, went to the other side and vainly tried to pull Whelks off the stick.

It was useless. 'Don't worry, my darling, I'll go and get some help,' she cried tearfully as she looked at the stick up his bum.

She managed to flag down a passing lorry on the main road that skirted the copse, and the driver said he would telephone for an ambulance. After what seemed an age, an ambulance arrived and, after the ambulance men had stopped laughing, they attempted to take the gearstick from out of Whelks' orifice. It wouldn't budge an inch, and a motor mechanic with a pick-up truck was sent for.

They towed the E-type into an all-night garage and it took an hour to unshackle the gearstick from its socket. Gingerly, the ambulance men lifted Whelks on to a stretcher, after cutting a hole in the canvas to allow the gearstick to poke through. Tearfully, as she held his hand. Carla said: 'I'm so sorry, my darling, this won't make any difference to our new-found love, will it?' Ashton turned his scarlet face away from her and whispered, 'Piss off.'

At that moment of time, Carla had an idea that she had lost him. The approaching war was forgotten in the wake of Ashton's plight and the gossips had a field day. The gearstick was removed in a clinic and Melanie forgave Ashton Whelks for his misdemeanour, and they were married at a church in Datchet three months later.

Carla's heart was broken and she sobbed in the privacy of her bedroom for over a week. At the finish, her pillow was so damp, there was a rainbow over her curtain rail. She took to the bottle and drank herself into a stupor. The reek of spirits was so heavy, the only plant that bloomed was hops. But time is something of a healer, and Carla, embittered and hard of heart, re-emerged into the world once more and found that people were too preoccupied with the political state of the country to worry over her tantrums.

Melanie and Ashton were still on honeymoon at Bognor Regis so at least she was spared the misery of seeing their happiness. Ashton had recovered from his accident in the E-type but apparently, when he had a bowel movement, he put brakes on his shoes.

Carla's father and mother opened their home to the Southern aristocracy and Red Butler was a frequent visitor. At one cocktail party to launch the formation of the Surrey Light Foot, Red Butler spoke to Carla and asked her to go to London with him. It was on the tip of her tongue to refuse but, just at that moment, Ashton Whelks and Melanie entered the room looking radiantly happy.

'Why not?' Carla shouted. She took hold of Red Butler's arm and they started dancing a Hungarian polka ... which was a trifle unusual because the band was playing the last waltz. Carla was tipsy and madly gay that evening and she flirted outrageously with the amused Red Butler.

Melanie buttonholed Carla in the ladies' powder room. Her obvious happiness was like a dagger in Carla's breast. 'Dear Carla, it doesn't seem right for one person to have so much, does it?' she whispered.

'I'm so happy I could cry.' Carla resisted the temptation to bang the lavatory seat down on Melanie's head and, through clenched teeth mouthed; 'Bless you, Melly. Why, fiddle-de-de, you deserve one another, my sweet.'

Melanie hugged Carla warmly. 'I notice that handsome Red Butler couldn't take his eyes off you.'

Carla shrugged her lovely shoulders at the sly reference. 'Oh, poo, he's not my beaú, but he makes a fine escort', Carla retorted, anxious to get away from Melanie. At last she escaped and, as she was about to go back to the party, Red Butler put her over his shoulder in a fireman's lift and stalked away with her into the gazebo. 'Put me down this instant' she screamed.

Butler merely chuckled and carried on, staggering under her weight. Once inside the summerhouse, he smothered her with kisses and, after a brief resistance, Carla found herself yielding to his advances.

What would have happened is best left to the imagination or Jackie Collins but, at the moment of having her knickers removed, loud curses and yells were heard coming from the house. Butler sprang to his feet, adjusted his Y-fronts and surgical belt and, with a hurried, 'Sorry, my dear' to Carla, he ran hot-foot to the house.

There he found the assembly stunned at the news they'd just heard on the Jimmy Young Radio Show: Northern troops had stolen a march on the South, thanks to Merrypepper's treachery, and they had crept into Fort Dunlop, on the edge of the M6, which was now in their hands.

'Ladies and gentlemen,' thundered a tall white-haired man who had taken command of the room. 'Please raise your glasses in a salute to our national unity. I give you – The South.' Roars of approval followed by the clink of tumblers greeted this short burst of oratory and the band struck up with the new anthem, 'A Foggy Day In London Town', and there wasn't a dry eye in the house. A white-faced lady, whose husband used to plant things in Burma, asked in a quavering voice; 'Does this mean war is inevitable?'

There was a thick silence for a moment, before the white-haired man spoke. 'Yes, I'm afraid it does, my dear lady. The South is about to fight the insurgency of the North.'

Somebody remarked that it would mean a come back for Vera Lynn, and Edwina Curry, who was drinking Diet Coke, said that the North didn't eat properly and wouldn't stand the pace. Melanie fainted with emotion and Ashton Whelks screwed up his eyes and walked into a nest of tables.

It was decided to have the Royal Family flown to Canada so as to eliminate any suggestion of bias on their part. Her Majesty The Queen was strongly in favour of retiring to Balmoral; His Royal Highness Prince Philip was keen to stay at Sandringham, and Princess Di wanted to stay in a flat close to Harrods in time for the winter sales. Prince Charles was worried about going bald and didn't know where he was and the rest of them wanted to sail about in the Royal yacht and lie low until Wimbledon started again.

Ethnic minorities were given a choice: support the area they'd settled in or be interned for the duration of the war when it came. In the North, Peabody-Brown's government conscripted all the Indians who'd settled in Bradford as labour battalions for the building of defence systems against any proposed attack; the Chinese communities were encouraged to do two days free laundry for brass-bandsmen, and West Africans were recruited to teach social workers the art of the rain dance. In the South, ethnic peoples took an oath, which meant they were 'Southern British' and therefore eligible for VAT and free bus passes if their cars were in dock.

Granada and Yorkshire Television beamed broadcasts only down as far as Knutsford, and 'Emmerdale' was given a prime viewing slot. Anyone foolhardy enough to attempt to receive television pictures from the South could be arrested and be drummed out of BUPA.

On Monday morning at six a.m. as the tepid rays of an invalid sun filtered through the low-lying nimbus, soldiers of the Third Bedfordshire Rangers fired off a salvo from their Second World War Lee-Enfield rifles at the daunting walls of Fort Dunlop, occupied by Northern troops, and although there were no casualties reported, a terrible fury erupted. Many historians, in the years to come, would pinpoint that incident as the real start to the Civil War. Southern artillery pounded the walls of Fort Dunlop for over an hour, demolishing large sections of the building and causing the defenders to scurry for cover in the lower section of the edifice. To further unnerve the Northern troops, the attackers played tapes of Chas and Dave relentlessly, and several men from Bolton deserted under the pressure of the cockney duo's accents.

After the artillery bombardment, the infantry charged across the central M6 barrier but had to wait until a lorry full of frozen prawns went past. This delay tended to remove the drama from the impassioned assault, and gave the defenders time for a brew. Finally, the infantry were in position and some hand grenades were lobbed at the main entrance but only one went off. It did little damage, apart from gelding a homeless hamster, and giving the Dunlop people a chance for a rates rebate.

Encouraged by the lack of resistance, the infantry started to scale the walls with ropes and ladders but the wily Northern defenders dropped tyre re-moulds on their heads and the troops had to retreat and scatter as the rubber missiles bounced merrily from the top-storey windows. Under the dome of night, the Southern attackers once more crept up to the very walls of the building and planted explosives around the base of the walls. With bated breath, they waited for the series of bangs; nothing happened. Gingerly, explosives experts wriggled forward to see what had gone wrong and found that the fuses had been dampened by a Dunlop guard dog peeing up a row of trees. Muttering oaths, the soldiers crept back to their lines with the wet fuses and badly bitten buttocks.

What had at first seemed to be a relatively easy military conquest now loomed as a knotty problem and it was decided, after a whist drive, to lay seige to Fort Dunlop. Whitehall was depressed by the whole incident and the Prime Minister cancelled his vasectomy operation.

Peabody-Brown's breakaway Northern government was delighted by the successful defence of Fort Dunlop and the North was jubilant. From Liverpool to Hull, the pubs were open all day, and in Scotland the haggis was piped in at every Marks and Spencer fashion show. Peabody-Brown was the hero of the day; those who had doubted the wisdom of going to war with the South now cheered him from every roof top. Peabody-Brown was the man of the hour, and he revelled in the glory of it all.

There were those who saw further than the paltry success at Fort Dunlop. After all, they argued, the South had the manpower and the resources – not to mention the ear of the international money markets. The headlong enthusiasm of the Northern armies, they said, could not be sustained. From out of the fog of cloud-cuckoo-land came all sorts of oddities who thought that some of Peabody-Brown's cracked ideas could be taken a step further. One idiot put forward the notion that a canal should be dug through the country at the Cheshire-Lancashire border and filled with piranha fish to keep intruders out. Fortunately, during a rally, he went rather peculiar and dropped dead in the arms of a part-time fireman. Another strange gentleman from Ormskirk declared on a radio chat show that Lancashire should be sold to Japan as a giant golf course. In his words on the air: 'It'll keep the yellow buggers happy and their minds off making transistors.'

Such was the fervour in the North that too many men wanted to join the new model army and stocks of uniforms and rifles were exhausted, so thousands of would-be recruits were sent home to see if their wives could run something up on a machine. The Royal Navy (what there was of it) was mainly based at Scapa Flow and on Peabody-Brown's orders it was commandeered by a retired tanker captain. All the sailors who held allegiance to the Southern cause were cast adrift in open boats. It was rumoured that most of them finished up in Sweden and became extras in blue movies.

THE CIVIL WAR

'We will do what we have to do and do it . . .
What is to do will be done and do it we
will. For what is done is done and do it we must
otherwise it won't get done.'
(Extract from a speech by Florence Bott)

Red Butler was proving invaluable to the South. His
grasp of the Northern mentality could not be bettered,
and he was gathering a fortune from grateful sources as
well as from governmental departments. He had all this,
and his plum take from whisky smuggling, to ensure his
riches – and yet he would have traded it all for one night
spent with Carla O'Mara. She kept him firmly at bay and
made no secret of the fact that she still desired Ashton
Whelks, who by this time had been made Poet Laureate
– his stirring odes of battle were on sale in every decent
newsagent's shop.

The war started with cautious troop movements
towards each other's borders. Meanwhile, the South

had laid siege to Fort Dunlop, starving the Northern lads of their meat pie and chips, and when the beer ran out they surrendered. The surrender came just in time, because the AA was receiving complaints about the tanks on the hard shoulder of the M6.

One of the biggest problems was trying to find out who supplied the money for the petrol needed to keep the tanks and lorries running. The Peabody-Brown rebel government was still buying two-star fuel on HP but, in the South, the Prime Minister stoutly maintained that the recently formed Army should have a whip-round for petrol and not rely on government hand-outs all the time. This political hot potato gave the North its edge, and whilst Southern generals and the like argued, the Northern troops under cover of darkness used a weapon far more terrible in its concept than the cobalt bomb – traffic cones.

They simply created one-way systems with thousands of red cones until it was impossible, without the help of those who had laid them, to go more than a hundred yards at a time. When Southern tanks and lorries tried to roll up the A1 or the M1, such was the confusion created by the placing of the cones that most of them finished up going back the way they'd come and a lot of them got fed up and played 'Space Invaders' in the motorway service stations. Under the command of General Harry Shireman, a Territorial officer and wholesale butcher from Ripon, three armoured regiments with infantry broke through a hastily erected barrier at the Nottingham turn-off on the M1. It was a bold move, because Nottinghamshire had declared its intent to remain neutral and was, as a matter of fact, charging Peabody-Brown ten pounds a week rental on his Robin Hood outfit. However, the invasion went ahead splendidly – and apart from a traffic warden putting a ticket on Shireman's tank turret – there was nothing done to impede the armoured thrust.

On and on the convoy rolled by day and by night, stopping only for the troops to have a pee and a game or two of al fresco bingo. It was outside Newton Pagnall that the first enemy soldiers could be seen, crouching behind a pile of sandbags. At Shireman's signal, the tanks ground to a halt and the twenty-pounder guns were swung into a firing position. Through a megaphone, Shireman shouted: 'Surrender or be wiped out.'

There was no reply from the Southern forces and Shireman ordered his gunner to open fire. The tank hadn't been used since Korea and the shell left the barrel of the gun in a noisy shoosh; the gun recoiled, and the end of it snapped off and fell into a ditch. The shell went off with a bang and blew a farmer's trousers off. The farmer played hell with Shireman and made him pay a fiver for damages. Red-faced and angry, Shireman ordered the infantry to charge the sandbagged emplacement but nobody could find the bugler to start off the charge, so the men sat down again.

General Orde-Grant, on his drive to the South, asked for paratroopers to be dropped behind a heavily defended Southern flank near Tewkesbury. A strong wind billowing across the hills caused the paratroopers to drift into Wales and several parachutes didn't open – which wasn't surprising, because nothing opens on Sunday in Wales.

None of the men with a defective chute were hurt because they all landed in a sewage filter bed and subsequently lost a lot of budding friendships in discos.

Owing to the many cut-backs in defence budgets under various governments in the past, it was a rueful shock to realize that bullets, shells and rocket missiles were in very short supply. Those the armies did have were so damp that when they were fired off they didn't explode and kill; they burst open and gave soldiers trench feet.

In the early days of the conflict, the warring armies threw stones at one another but they had to give that up because school children at playtime had a much better aim than the troops and the armies had to run away from the hail of well-targeted brick ends and pebbles. One thing was made abundantly clear: the Northern armies were doing better than those of the South. One of the problems was that Southern troops had paid deposits on their holidays in Tenerife, and weren't always on hand for the major battles. By early autumn, the North had driven deep into the South: Watford fell after only two days of fighting and all Kentucky Fried Chicken vendors were turned into pork butchers. General Orde-Grant did a flanking movement around General Lee's Southern army in the Cotswolds, and raced on for Berkshire in a wide sweeping pincer manoeuvre that netted thousands of prisoners and shares in Trustee Savings.

The Fifth Column in the South infiltrated Northern positions and created havoc by opening betting shops offering wagers on hire purchase, and cross-breeding whippets with airedales. But the overall picture was one of indifference by the South, and the Great Retreat was on. Quite a large section of citizens now under Northern rule actually enjoyed the life-style they now were subjected to: every pub had a three-piece band in it, there were a lot of talent shows about, and Max

Bygraves cut a record of Lancashire ditties and bought a block of flats in Rotherham. Margaret Thatcher came out of retirement, took the bottle from her husband's mouth, and they took up Cumberland-style wrestling.

The good life had ceased to exist at Tara. Enemy troops had been reported digging in ten miles from Windsor and there was an air of despair settling on the O'Mara mansion.

Melanie was pregnant; Carla was sullen and drinking heavily and Ashton Whelks couldn't look at a gearstick without bursting into tears. Mr O'Mara became a recluse after smashing up his warehouse full of glazed bidets, and Mrs O'Mara smiled a lot and knitted scarves.

Carla sensed that her family was falling apart at the seams and she began to look forward to seeing Red Butler. Although she still privately called him 'White Trash' she found his company at least amusing, even when he tried to give her the occasional grope. She knew that Red Butler visited the brothels set up by the Northern forces and she despised him for that, but that didn't stop her from secretly wondering what he was like in bed.

Food supplies were drying up in the supermarkets of the South. The only available nourishment was that gleaned from black-marketeers who stole curry and chips from Northern depots. Before long, many sensitive Southern stomachs were suffering from a new plague: 'Gandhi's Revenge'. There wasn't a single rectum that didn't feel abrasive in Henley-on-Thames, and those who tried to live on cowheel or mushy peas underwent so much suffering from colonic wind that joke shops

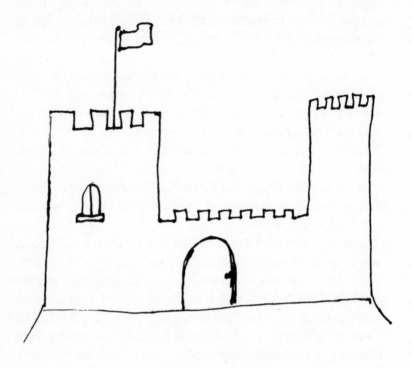

Fort Goole, once an apricot warehouse (retail only) which became the focal point of the siege of Hull. It was built on a whim by a pools winner who was going quite bald. The fort was a main obstacle to the Southern Army and it smelt. (*Sketch was drawn from memory by Harry Emsley, a juggler, copies sell at most markets during a cattle-drive*).

in seaside resorts made a fortune out of selling fart powder.

Melanie's pregnancy was going badly. She was constantly in pain and Carla reluctantly took over Melanie's duties at the hospital. There were not many soldiers injured in battle, most of them were suffering from flat feet through marching everywhere. But Carla hated nursing as a job, and formed a troupe of entertainers who went round the wards singing and juggling. This was so successful that Carla was offered a part in a pantomime at Lewisham, *Mother Goose*, but had to turn the offer down when her father finally went barmy and tried to strangle a horse.

Carla's mother had a nervous breakdown and was sent to the Isle of Wight for treatment and Tara fell into disrepair. Only one faithful servant remained on the premises, a one-legged parlourmaid who had once made hops for a brewery.

It was a time of great melancholy. Where once had been a drift of laughter, there was now only silence from those empty rooms of Tara. The once proud and haughty gardens, now raped and brutalized by the encroaching weeds, disfigured the majestic sweep of the house. It was a time of great melancholy, and most of the drains were blocked. From a distance, the sound of cannon-fire and the sporadic cough of a rifle formed a sonic backcloth to the desolate scene.

It was a time of great melancholy and Carla's parlourmaid, in a fit of pique after eating a banana fritter, fell asleep on her water-bed. When the room caught fire, she was poached to death. Carla was alone in the world and her heart was breaking as she buried the parlourmaid in the privets. Melanie was still bellowing with her pregnancy and Ashton kept walking into lamp posts.

Refugees who staggered past the O'Mara estate told of General Shireman's march through Guildford. Tearful stragglers narrated the story of Milton Keynes being bulldozed to make way for a permanent exhibition of

Yorkshire heritage, including free trips to Bridlington for pensioners and tours round the Scarborough lifeboat. The homeless wretches spoke of endless 'stag dinners' thrown by the Northern troops, and how genteel Southern ladies were paid to take their frocks off on stage and do impressions of Denis Healey.

The ghastly recital of humiliation and the shame of the once-elegant South made Carla's stomach turn. She no longer went to see her father – the old firebrand had locked himself in a box and only came out to go to the lavatory. At last he was taken away by a Securicor van in a box labelled 'Fragile – This Way Up' and delivered to an institution specializing in the treatment of men with his complaint.

But there were stories of valour, above and beyond the call of duty. During the battle for Harlow New Town, a corporal in the East Dorset Light Infantry who had been captured by soldiers of the Pontefract Mounted Foot, single-handedly beat six of them at three-card brag and stole their dentures.

Surrounded by a regiment of Plymouth Marines, a young recruit from the Barnsley Volunteers shouted that he would wear red trousers so that the enemy would not see the blood from his wounds; the rest of the Barnsley lads shouted that they'd wear khaki.

From both sides in this sickening conflict came reports of bravery and heroism as well as stories of inhuman conduct. Captured troops from Dorking were made to swallow lumps of cold bread pudding and slivers of black tripe in the prison camps at Doncaster; good-looking young men from the East End of London were made to suffer the indignity of parading naked in front of Northern women at hen parties, when the colder climate of the North caused the chaps to develop high-pitched voices and acute embarrassment at the shrinkage of their personal fixtures.

Three Lancastrian signalmen captured in Hertfordshire were dragged along Oxford Street by a gay Pearlie King and forced into Selfridge's and made to shout, 'Woolworth's forever.'

There was a growing concern about the listless and apathetic state of the Southern Army; on every front there was a general retreat, and it began to look as if London would soon be invaded by the Northern forces.

The only good aspect of the war was that as yet, apart from cuts caused by stones, nobody had been killed or injured on the battlefield. This was mainly because thousands of soldiers were wearing pin-striped suits and nobody knew who was fighting whom. The Northern uniforms made everybody laugh, so the fighting men of the North sold them to kids for Hallowe'en, and put the money into building societies.

Likewise, the uniforms of the South created titters – and, as any ex-warrior knows only too well, there's nothing worse than leading a bayonet charge against an enemy shaking with mirth. In some cases, opposing troops got together and swapped mother-in-law jokes and one general was so upset by it all that he threw his hat away and became an evangelist in Cardiff.

Europeans were totally baffled by it all. The German press demanded over and over again in print: 'How did they get away from Dunkirk?' The French merely shrugged their shoulders, asked what could one expect from a race who only talked to each other about the weather, and got on with ignoring the rest of humanity. On the world's stock markets, shares dropped so low they were pinning mice to the floor, and the pound sterling went down lower in value than the Madras rupee.

Meanwhile, Windsor capitulated and the castle was turned into a replica of a Northern Workingmen's Club. The Southern government didn't know what the hell to do and the Prime Minister's wife started with piles.

It was the burning of Aldershot that finally galvanized the South into action; reluctantly, the Prime Minister sent for the one man who had an affinity with both sides: Red Butler. He had been wooing Carla O'Mara in Henley-on-Thames, and twice she'd had to brain him with a Hoover to stop his torrid advances. Carla had had her share of problems; Melanie had given birth to a sickly male baby, and because of Melanie's health, Carla had to look after the infant as well as look for Ashton's contact lenses. Whelks' eyesight was getting so foggy that on one occasion he tried to whistle but couldn't find his lips. He was also becoming vague, and Carla's heart went out to him, but she still couldn't get him between the sheets.

All around her, Carla saw the destruction of a way of life ... a way of life that could never be the same again. From across the gently swelling hills she could hear the roll of cannon fire. Often, on occasions, she would hear the curses of troops creeping through exceptionally moist cow-pats, and her heart would sink at the sight of refugees shuffling playing-cards in tented casinos run by the Toc-H. Where were all her beaux of yesterday? Those reckless swains with the bold eyes? Harold Thrimball, always laughing, always eager for life, but now a sad worn-out captain with a crop of boils and a hernia. Where was he? Lying in wait for the approach of the dreaded Northern Troops? Or worse still, waiting for the eight thirty-two train to arrive in Swanley on time from Victoria?

Would she ever again dance lightheartedly with Kurt Cackenfester, that handsome son of a German draughtsman? He had scorned the opportunity of going back to Hamburg when the war started; instead he had joined the Orpington branch of a national deckchair company to instruct their employees how to wake up early in a hotel, creep down to the swimming-pool and bung a pile of towels on every seat facing the sun in the true Teutonic fashion of holiday-making. Carla closed her eyes and swayed at the nostalgic memories of being held tightly by Cecil Forfoarby-Pilkington-Rash, whose entire family had died of embarrassment. Dear Cecil, so tall and slender, good-looking in an odd sort of way; having no teeth never detracted from the sweep of his noble forehead, nor did the hump on his shoulder or the bandy legs offend the observer. Some rude types would comment on Cecil's complete baldness and the squint in his right eye, but they oft served to enhance his appeal to the ladies. Dear Cecil . . . Carla smiled softly to herself as she remembered holding her nose every time Cecil had his accidental bowel movement in Tesco's. Carla pulled herself together. What was the point of torturing her mind with pictures of the past?

The distant thunder of the cannonade caused Carla to tremble violently and she hurriedly withdrew into the bedroom. Red Butler's face swam before her vision, and her legs quivered at the thought of the man. Some thoughtless friend had mentioned that Butler

was 'Extremely well-endowed, dearie,' and went on to
suggest that the man was a sort of human tripod. At
this recollection, Carla blushed and took deep breaths.
Outside, in the still air, menace hung like an invisible
drape and, in the thicket, a cat was sick again.

The Prime Minister paced the floor in the office at
Number 10 Downing Street as he poured out his tales
of woe to Red Butler, who sat on the Chesterfield
smoking an expensive cigar and watching the Prime
Minister prowl up and down with amusement.

'Frankly, Butler, the situation is extremely dangerous.
You and I both know that Peabody-Brown should
be certified, but he's imbued the North with such a
fanaticism, that this country of ours is in grave peril.'
The PM paused and sipped a little Bovril. 'We are the
laughing-stock of the world and something has to be
done. Otherwise this great nation of ours will become
another branch of Disneyland. You, Mr Butler (or may
I call you Albert?), have the ear of both sides in this
ridiculous dispute, and I am willing to listen and pay for
any ideas you may possess to get this country sane again.'

Red Butler knew in his heart of hearts that Peabody-
Brown was a nutcase and the Prime Minister was correct
when he said that Britain was in peril; that also he knew.
There was a long silence, and then Butler spoke in his
hoarse tones: 'Prime Minister, the only way to halt the
North is to divide their union, and that is to be the first
aim. All I want out of it, should I succeed in doing so, is a
villa in Cannes and a weekly food basket from Fortnum
& Mason. The initial step is to garner support for the
South in the USA.'

The PM jerked his head towards Butler. 'Do you honestly think you could do that? Up to now the American government has ignored the situation. There hasn't been a word from them since the Palladium cancelled Johnny Mathis.'

Butler smiled and replied, 'Get me a seat on Concorde and leave the rest to me.' The two men shook hands and Butler strode out.

On his way to Heathrow the following night, Butler watched Londoners preparing to defend their city against the encroaching tide of Northern barbarism. Once again, as in the blitz of old, London was united against a common foe. Despite himself, Red Butler felt a sense of pride in the dogged pursuit to hold back the enemy.

Trenches were being dug in the Mall; Regent Street was lined with sandbags and people were singing: 'Let's All Go Down The Strand.' Posters with slogans had been tied to lampposts, slogans that read: 'No Chip Butties For Us', 'The Bloody North Can Stick Their Eccles Cakes.' Heady words indeed from a beleaguered populace, stirring the blood of a nation with its back to the wall!

Arrived in New York, Red Butler telephoned a friend of his who ran the biggest public relations business on Madison Avenue. Butler swiftly outlined some of his ideas to his friend George Carter, who had many friends in London, and he became enthused with Red Butler's plan to shatter the unity of the triumphant North.

In essence the plan that Butler had thought out was quite a simple one. Knowing that most Americans felt the need for a traditional background like that of the average Britisher, Butler's idea was to fake the discovery of historic papers that would give Polish–American and other Americans of immigrant family backgrounds the soothing knowledge that they could claim Scottish ancestry. Butler knew that the fiery Scots, who hated a government based in London such a long way from Edinburgh, would be the fiercest fighters against it. If they could be prised away from the breakaway Northern Union, it would be the first step in the defeat of the cockeyed Peabody-Brown.

Television programmes were set to spread the phoney information and before long Americans with names like Kowlowsky or Giovanni were proudly stunned to learn that Kowlowsky, for instance, came from a very old Celtic word meaning 'man from Glasgow.' Every Italo-American in the Bronx now was aware that he was distantly related to Rob Roy's sister. With a web of deceit, Americans were told that it wasn't Columbus who stumbled upon the New World, but Eric The Peculiar, a Scottish navigator from Inverness – and, within weeks, New York had sold out of kilts.

The next move was to instil into the American public the fear that Bonnie Scotland was being led astray by the other breakaway members of the Anarchist Union, and that they had only joined in desperation at their economic status. Big business now put pressure on the President and his administration to send aid to Scotland, providing that the Scots would revert to being what they were before, if you see what I mean.

It worked to perfection. All through the month of November dollars poured into Scotland; American businessmen in tartan kilts and sporrans took over disused factories and the Clyde shipyards, and unemployment dropped to zero. So happy were the Americans at finding themselves a part of historic traditions that they scrapped the custom of having a turkey for Thanksgiving, and ate Arbroath smokies and bannock cakes instead. Even large sections of the American coloured community played jazz on bagpipes and sang 'Mama's Liddle Baby Loves Shortenin' Bread . . . Och Aye.'

Finally, bemused and happy, Scotland declared herself a neutral, and Celtic and Rangers played a game of football without one foul.

It was a bitter blow for the Anarchist Union; Peabody-Brown felt betrayed, and grew more bitter and twisted than ever before. Scottish soldiers simply went back home from the battlefields in hired vans, and that was that. Some Northern troops managed to invade the outskirts of Finchley, but the price of things there sent them running back. London was saved by the cost of living.

With the booming Scottish economy now in full swing, thousands of new jobs were created and Scotland's American benefactors started casting glances at Tyneside for men to fill the positions in the growing industries.

This gave Red Butler another opportunity to deliver a blow to the Anarchist Union solidarity. He persuaded Japanese distillers to put money into Newcastle breweries, because he convinced them that water from the River Wear would make Japanese whisky more potent and desirable, particularly if they gave away a camera with every ploughman's lunch served in a pub.

The news of this shook the giant companies in the Land of the Rising Sun, and Toshiba opened two huge microwave oven discount stores with free packets of frozen peas with every sale in Gateshead. Ere long, vibrant young Japanese businessmen were studying how to speak Geordie in night schools, as well as giving ju-jitsu lessons to shy traffic wardens. It became common-place to see hordes of Japanese men and women bowing to each and saying in their attractive hissing tones, 'W'ar yer ganna 'ere man? Arsoo.'

The result of this fresh invasion of prosperity was of course inevitable. The whole of the North–East of England left the Union cause and gave allegiance back to Parliament, with a bit left over for Nagasaki. Some people might have thought that the sight of hulking Americans in kilts walking about with tiny Japs dressed in flat caps and mufflers trotting at their side would have given things a carnival air, but nobody took any notice of them – although there was a faint protest at seeing Pakistani formation teams dancing the minuet. The departure of Tyne-Tees from the Northern rebel government made Cheshire think again, and two days before Christmas the county withdrew its support for Peabody-Brown and asked the House of Commons for a vote of confidence and a subsidy for cheese-making.

The swift disintegration of The Anarchist Right Wing Left Of Centre Worker's Union Party came at a time when the South was reeling. Dover had surrendered to a platoon of Oldham Pioneers and had given the lads a free trip on a ferry to Calais as well as a basket of halibut. Windsor, Maidenhead and Richmond had fallen, and the citizens of Golder's Green had sold the borough to the North with ten per cent off suit lengths. Now, suddenly, only Lancashire and Yorkshire were left in the Union. They hadn't enough troops to carry on any longer. For the first time in the civil struggle, there was

Minnie Shufflebottom the notorious bordello keeper from Scunthorpe who passed vital information to the enemy in jars of Bovril. An expert bugler with a mail order chamber orchestra, Minnie had the confidence of General Ackroyd who commanded a troop of piano accordian mechanics at Pontin's. She was taken into custody, tried by court martial and sentenced to three months without cocoa in a Blackpool boarding house. (*Sketch by courtesy of Arnold Postlewaithe's mother*)

more than a gleam of hope for the Southern cause of rightful government.

All of this meant nothing to Carla; her every waking moment was spent yearning for Ashton Whelks. Melanie's baby was still sickly, and Tara was now occupied by Northern infantry officers who kept themselves to themselves, but drove Carla insane with their brass band practise. She moved into a deserted bungalow after finally snapping under the decibel horror of a cornet solo and a duet for euphonium and flugelhorn.

Melanie's health was improving only slightly, and Carla decided she would take her to her aunt's cottage

in Hampshire. Struggling under the weight of the invalid Melanie, Carla managed to get her in the back seat of her E-type Jaguar and, with apprehension at the thought of the dangers ahead, she drove away from the stricken ruins that had once been Henley-on-Thames, and cautiously motored south.

She would never forget the appalling scenes that she witnessed. She saw drunken Northern soldiers asleep in the gutters, Southern black marketeers selling cartons of clotted cream to bedraggled housewives who were sick of the thick north-country custard; children begging for money to buy video cassettes. She saw soldiers of the South taken as prisoners of war; these once proud and gallant men, who would gallop to battle at the drop of a trilby, were now forced to attend Tupperware parties and groom homing pigeons. With a shudder, she saw prostitutes who'd gone too far on the F-plan diet parading around with cards strung to their jumpers which read, 'In case of sex, this way up.'

Had the world gone mad, she asked herself, as she surveyed the nightmare scene. The days of ballgowns and whispered promises on Georgian staircases seemed so far away now, as did the kisses stolen to violins strumming a Hoffmann barcarole . . . Had those days really existed, or were they phantoms of her imagination? She shifted the wad of chewing tobacco from one side of her mouth to the other and concentrated on her driving.

Her heart began to thump as the curtains of night drew across the landscape. The tall poplars escorting the rustic track to Melanie's aunt's cottage seemed to crouch over the headlight beam from her car. She stole a glance at the petrol gauge; nearly empty. She stifled a tremor of panic but it jolted back when she saw faces peering at her from behind bushes. 'Please, God', she almost shouted to herself, 'Don't let me run out of fuel now.' God did not heed her prayer, and the E-type spluttered to a halt.

Melanie was asleep in the rear seat, and didn't respond when Carla shook her shoulder. In the illumination from her headlights, Carla saw a man approaching the vehicle. A sudden calm came over her. If he raped her, she would lie back and think of England, or at least a win on Littlewoods. She closed her eyes and gripped the steering wheel tightly and tensed as the car door was opened.

'What in blazes are you doing down here, Carla?' a familiar hoarse voice inquired.

She opened her eyes wide and stared at the puzzled face of Albert 'Red' Butler. Then she fainted. When she came to, she found herself supine on a settee with floral covers in an old-fashioned room with wooden beams and a stone fireplace, in front of which sat a cat that had just been sick in a thicket. Melanie was stroking her forehead and Red Butler was holding out a tumbler of spirits to her. 'What happened?' she whispered.

Melanie smiled and replied gently, 'You fainted, dearest, and Mr Butler awoke me and I led the way to my aunt's cottage as Mr Butler carried you in his arms.'

Carla glanced slyly at Red Butler and she blushed most winningly. 'Fiddle-de-de,' she snorted. 'What a silly little fool you must think I am, to be sure.' She saw the naked lust in Red Butler's eyes and a hot fever stole through her loins.

The men she had seen on that narrow country lane had been Southern troops regrouping in readiness for a counter-attack against the Northern forces. Red Butler had taken a party of Japanese businessmen to a Holiday

Inn for a ritual hari-kiri get-together with drinks at
'Happy Hour' prices.

Carla was hustled to bed by a very anxious Melanie
and, despite her protests that the excitement had removed her tiredness, once she was between the clean
crisp sheets, Carla commenced to descend into an abyss
of untroubled slumber. Melanie kissed her friend lightly
and, as a last gesture of tenderness, with the hem of her
underslip wiped the rim of the embossed chamber pot.

'How is she, Melanie?' asked Red Butler.

Melanie smiled at the concern in his question. 'She's
asleep now, Mr Butler, the poor dear. She's so brave, is
she not?' She threw him a sly glance as she spoke.

Red Butler felt the need to confide in someone about
his hunger for the love of Carla. 'Melanie, what do I have
to do in order to win Carla?'

Butler paused, eager to hear Melanie's reply. She saw
an almost waif-like expression flit across his rugged face.
He really was a very handsome man, she thought to
herself; he had a most interesting left eye, the right one
kept looking at it. 'Oh, Mr Butler, she'll come round. I
know she will. Such beauty as hers is bound to be wilful
at times.'

As she spoke, Melanie remembered the joy that Carla
had brought into people's lives. Melanie recalled with a
smile how Carla had once tied her purple knickers over
her head and had gone to a fancy-dress party as a plum.
As a leggy colt, Carla used to have her parents in fits of
laughter when she stood in the chip pan and pretended
to be a dipstick. What a child she had been, Melanie
mused. She saw in her mind's eye again the tears on
Carla's cheeks when she had failed to wrestle an ox to the
floor during a garden fête; of how she had often rammed

her father's top hat over a pig's head whilst standing in a bucket of warm Horlicks.

Melanie remembered ruefully how all the young men had adored Carla, whilst she had been such a wallflower. Hurt came into Melanie's eyes when she remembered she had been such a plain Jane as a baby that her father had put shutters on her pram, but Carla had been so beautiful as a toddler that Mr O'Mara had had her kidnapped to get her photograph in the papers. Bitter-sweet memories indeed . . .

Melanie shuddered when she recalled that, as a teenager, she had been so fat, when a boy danced with her he usually sat on her hip. No wonder she had been a wallflower! She used to wait for somebody to ask her to waltz for so long she stood in a bag of bone-meal. No, it had always been Carla who got the boys; but at least she, Melanie, had Ashton Whelks. She returned to the present, and realized that she must have been remembering the past and talking about it out loud because Red Butler was asleep with cotton wool in his ears.

Melanie tiptoed outside the cottage and sat on the swing in her aunt's garden. Auntie had been a wonderful person, and Melanie missed her so. She had been such an interesting lady with her job making cork freckles for clowns on a low income. Melanie's uncle had been a drunken librarian, whose only claim to fame was that he could yodel in three languages and recite the Lord's Prayer whilst drinking a pint of cider.

He died as he would have no doubt wished: during a Thames-side barbeque party he had fallen into a vat of brandy and perished despite the fact that he had got out of the vat six times to go to the gent's urinal. So much brandy had he imbibed, that three weeks after he was buried they could still smell his breath at the inquest. He left Melanie's aunt penniless but she contrived to get him buried on hire purchase, a sort of 'Go Now . . . Pay Later.' To her horror, Auntie found she couldn't keep up the funeral repayments and she received a rebuking letter from the undertaker which stated that, if she didn't pay off the instalments, up her husband would come.

As she swung up and down, Melanie remembered her proud aunt disdaining help from relatives and friends, and getting a job towing caravans around the country and doing well at it until the rope pulled her teeth out.

Her reverie was halted when she saw Ashton Whelks groping his way up the garden path. Melanie jumped off the swing and, with arms outstretched, ran to her beloved husband shouting girlishly, 'Ashton, oh Ashton, my love!'

'Darling', he replied, and started to embrace a tree.

Daily, the suffering increased as the war escalated. Hundreds of troops, on both sides of the conflict, went down with shingles, gout and overdrafts. There was nothing but gloom and misery in the radio bulletins; *Sun* newspaper readers voted Samantha Fox 'Miss Bayonet Frog', and she took her blouse off for a pensioner who'd come up on Ernie.

Fierce fighting raged backwards and forwards, across town and country, brother fought brother in terrible encounters whose names would sear the memory for all time. For many years to come, men would say in awed tones, 'I was there.' History would record the major conflicts of the Civil War, but would overlook the carnage in the smaller confrontations such as that of

'Willie's Dyke'. There, both armies wallowed in the silt of a ruined septic tank in an effort to win high ground and a chance to face a strong wind. Only those who fought there will remember Hackett's Corset factory in Todmorden, where the Southern forces threw bales of elastic at Northern infantrymen and sixteen men twanged to death.

Many soulful songs would emerge from the war, songs sung by tired, weary men, men haunted by the Grim Reaper. There were songs to march by, songs to charge by and songs to die by. The celebrated Highgate poet, Frank Smellie, recalls in a voice charged with emotion the night he heard a platoon of soldiers from Dewsbury harmonize the Northern battle hymn 'She Was Only A Tobacconist's Daughter, But She Was The Best Shag In The Shop.' A banjo-playing nun composed a dirge which nearly got played by Jimmy Savile, just before he was shot off his cigar:

Give me a home where the buffalo roam
And you'll always need a shovel and bucket.
Where seldom is heard a discouraging word
Until you slide in the yuk and shout . . . oh bother.

Arlene Du Pres, the famous television star, and her all-girl steel pipe band had an audience of thousands in tears the first time she sang the stirring Bagshot Chant at a rally in Croydon.

An old barrow-boy from Mill Hill
Swallowed an atomic pill.
They found his barrow in Harrow
And his nuts up a tree in Brazil.

But no song, however pleasing to the ear, could stifle the din of war. The young men flocked to the colours for a chance to be part of history ... How many would return? Most of them, actually, because the main recruiting centres for both armies were on strike.

As is the case in all troubles, it was the women of the country who bore the brunt. The war had left good coffee in short supply and coffee mornings became a drag; women found it difficult to gossip for any length of time without Mellow Bird's or Nescafé Fine Blend.

Food wasn't too scarce, but most of it was of a poor quality. Horse meat was eaten a lot – so much, in fact, that a lot of children began to complain of a saddle rash. Householders now grew their own vegetables as the supply from the farms dried up. All agriculture was under direct military jurisdiction and if anyone was foolhardy enough to steal a beetroot, the offender stood a good chance of losing his or her celery, which could be a turnip for the book. That happened to a Swede and the punishment chilled him to the marrow. Nobody suspected this sort of thing was happening until there was a government leek.

Children were encouraged to eat plenty of greens, it was nice to see them sprout and also the greens kept them from being off colour.

So, then, did the nation stagger on through its darkest hour and in 'Coronation Street' Ken Barlow continued to be a complete idiot.

THE MYSTERY OF
ARNOLD POSTLEWAITHE

'What is it that makes it what it is?
Why is it, or why not? Is that it? I think not for it is.
Is that it then they may say it is.'
(Extract from a speech by Florence Bott)

Peabody-Brown was in a foul mood and his staff kept their distance from him. His mood was quite understandable; his Anarchist Union was coming apart at the seams and even some of his staunchest supporters were having grave doubts about the much-heralded Northern victory.

Already there was a stiffening of resistance in the South, and news had just arrived that Richmond was under attack by a recently formed regiment of West End accountants who were undermining the spirit of the Lancashire occupying troops by showering them with leaflets that set out a list of tax dodges and solid unit trust investments. There had been several cases of Lancashire

soldiers deserting to the enemy, lured by promises of Cup
Final tickets and a leg-over in Soho.

Morale wasn't all that it should have been in the North
during this harrowing period; even the invasion of Devon
and the take-over of a Cornish pixie factory didn't lift the
spirits one iota.

One of the main problems, of course, as Easter
approached, was the new-found Scottish prosperity.
Whereas before Scottish holiday-makers had flooded
Blackpool's cheaper boarding-houses, bringing their
own booze and tins of salmon, they now arrived at
the resort in Rolls Royces with enough money to buy the
boarding-houses and keep the landladies on as cleaners.
As Mrs Pickle, Blackpool's leading spokeswoman for the
boarding-house association, said, 'The buggers come 'ere
now and they are demanding sheets on the beds and
cocoa at night!' Mrs Pickle was visibly moved when
she was wildly applauded after demonstrating how to
slice boiled ham with a razor and correct usage of a
waterproof teabag. Blackpool's inhabitants, faced with
the rationing of cooked meats and beef-and-onion pies,
began to wonder just who was supposed to be winning
the war.

Scarborough, that famous old resort, suffered the same
fate as Blackpool except that its problem was with an
influx of wealthy Geordies. They came to the town and
deliberately paid over the odds for donkey rides and
plates of dressed crab, and made the Yorkshire holiday-
maker feel like a pauper. Questions were being asked
amongst the ordinary folk of Lancashire and Yorkshire;
questions the likes of, 'Even if the Union wins, what have
we got out of it?' Many responsible people were saying
that the Union should give up and a lot wanted to know

why the Union couldn't get aid from a foreign country. Over the ensuing weeks the news from the various fronts became more depressing; many of the rebel Union soldiers who had been stationed for long periods in the South had come back on leave with stories so terrible that bingo halls were observing a one-minute silence before calling out a full house.

There was irrefutable evidence that Northern soldiers had developed prostate trouble through drinking Southern-brewed beer; evidence that London-based commando units had put super-glue in Yorkshire Puddings *en route* to Union outposts, so that hundreds of rebel troops were now communicating with one another in sign language. So great was the unrest that Peabody-Brown's cabinet met in an emergency debate in Leeds.

Peabody-Brown, in his suit of Lincoln green, sat at the head of the long polished table and listened to the furore around him. He glowered at his cabinet and his insanity grew. He heeded not his military staff who urged him to recall the rebel forces to the North; he listened not to the urgent demands from sensible men for an end to the partition . . . Peabody-Brown paid no attention. His cabinet finally ceased to argue, and it came as no surprise to them when Peabody-Brown leapt to his feet and called them all traitors. With that, the door was flung open, and his personal bodyguards marched in, burly men in Lincoln green with staves and quivers of arrows, all of them singing 'Greensleeves'.

The news that Peabody-Brown had arrested his cabinet created high jubilation in London. The Prime Minister was so elated, he gave Neil Kinnock an exploding cigar. Kinnock as usual didn't even notice when it went off. Victory was in the air – Peabody-Brown had finally gone off his chump! Surely, it was argued, the solid Northern folk would realize that further ideas for a breakaway Union must now be in ashes?

The Prime Minister was also encouraged by his military advisers who told him that, at last, Southern forces were advancing on all fronts. Richmond had surrendered, and Windsor was once again in Parliament's control. The town was once more crammed with American tourists in kilts waving claymores at little Japanese Datsun workers in their bib and brace overalls and flat caps. The Japs were heard to say, many times: 'W'ay we'ar ganning doon 'ere 'coos w'ay fed up wee bloody Sunderland. Arshoo.'

Timidly, tourists from all over the world started to drift back to London now that the war scare had receded. They found themselves completely baffled by the spectacle of Japs in mufflers and clogs, Geordies in kimonos, Scotsmen wearing ten-gallon hats and cowboy boots, and hulking Americans sporting sporrans and plumed berets. As one diminutive Algerian put it, 'I thought I was in the middle of a Peruvian Inca festival.' Hoteliers in the Lake District pleaded with Peabody-Brown to do something, but it was difficult to get hold of him because he was living up an elm in a park. Something had to be done, and damned quickly, otherwise the North was going to be worse off than ever. Thus began the plot to get rid of Peabody-Brown.

Melanie and her baby returned from her aunt's cottage in Hampshire, invited by Carla to live with her. Ashton Whelks had proceeded beyond embracing innocent trees. He turned gay. Melanie had cried for days when she saw Ashton fumble his way out of an optician's shop wearing her best frock. In vain she had implored him to stay with her, if only for the sake of the baby, but the weak wretch had whined that he was in love with a Dutch teenage ventriloquist who had recently come fourth on 'Opportunity Knocks'.

So moved had Carla been when she saw Melanie's distress that she had gone to see the ventriloquist to plead with him to jilt Ashton Whelks. The simpering Dutch youth had told Carla to 'Get stuffed!' What angered Carla was that he had said it without moving his lips.

Life slowly returned to Tara after the last of the rebel troops retreated to the sound of a brass band playing 'Yes, We Have No Bananas'. Carla felt no hatred towards the soldiers, but secretly she vowed that if she ever saw a trombone or a trumpet again, she'd go on a sponsored suicide.

By late summer, the house was looking its old self again, though the gardens were still in a state of disrepair. Carla cajoled her neighbours to lend her their gardeners, and lumps of groundsel were being wrenched from the lawns. The institution suggested to Carla that it might act as therapy for her father, if he returned home. Carla thought it a splendid idea because Mr O'Mara wasn't responding to treatment and kept trying to eat his feet.

With trembling limbs, Carla stood outside the house on the day they brought her daddy home. Mistily, she watched the white-coated attendants lift his box on to the driveway and unscrew it. Her father tottered out of the box wearing only spats and a Panama hat. 'Oh, Daddy!' Carla screamed, and ran to embrace her father.

The old man took no notice of her, he simply gazed at the extensively damaged lawns and, with a whoop, he

A Cheshire cabin full of mincemeat, built on stilts to avoid the poll tax. The cabin was the scene of fierce fighting in the latter half of the Civil War, particularly among estate agents. After the War, the cabin became a shrine to a dwarf who fell off a skirting-board. (*Sketch by one of the Pickles family*)

got down on his hands and knees and started chewing the grass.

Carla ran to help him to his feet but the attendants stopped her from doing so. One of them, a kindly-faced middle-aged man, said in a low voice, 'Miss O'Mara, let him do it. We know him so well, and he thinks he's a lawn-mower. Let him be.'

Stunned, Carla nodded her head dumbly as she saw her parent chewing away in a straight line. Already there was a marked difference to the length of the grass.

The nice attendant patted Carla's shoulder. 'He's happy now and, looking at the other side of it, he will save you pounds in mushroom compost. You won't have to buy a lawn-mower either now, will you?'

As she watched her wonderful daddy on his hands and knees with his naked backside in the air, she realized the wisdom of the attendant's words. 'Will he be able to have his old bedroom back?' Carla asked him.

The man shook his head. 'No, Miss O'Mara, he will still live and sleep in his box, so I suggest you place it in the shade and leave his food on a tray.' The man paused and hesitated, choosing his next words. 'His diet has changed somewhat, Miss Carla,' he said. 'Now, he's very fond of raw cow's legs and crocus bulbs. One word of caution, however, make him wear boots in case he fancies nibbling his toes for dessert.'

'I cannot thank you enough, sir.' said Carla.

The man smiled gently. 'I understand these poor devils so well, my dear. For many years I was one of them. Indeed, even now, I'm only on a sort of probation before I'm finally released. That's why they made me an attendant – to see how I cope with the outside world.' He stroked his chin, and resumed. 'I am to be discharged next week and I can say, quite categorically, thanks to deep electric cerebral treatment, that my mental processes are now above the average intellect, and I shall soon go back to my old job in a solicitor's office.'

Carla hugged him closely, tears rolling down her face. 'Oh, I'm so happy for you,' she whispered as the man saluted and started to walk back to the ambulance. Carla waved and shouted, 'Were you a solicitor, then?'

The man turned. 'No, I was a teapot,' he yelled back.

*

Her father was in his element and soon the lawns were trim and almost back to their old standards. Carla attempted to get her father to wear trousers, especially after an Afghan hound tried to mount him, but the old man was stubborn. If she pushed him too much he would jump into his box and blow raspberries at her.

Mrs O'Mara never answered her daughter's letters and, when Carla heard that her mother was a drug dealer in a Darby and Joan club on the Isle of Wight, she washed her hands of her.

The war had certainly taken its toll, Carla thought to herself. Television and radio broadcasts were now back to normal, with 'Panorama' and re-runs of 'The Wombles' as firm favourites. The news was heartening; all rebel forces had been ousted from the South, and Watford had just been liberated. Lancashire and York-shire were totally alone, and the South was preparing an invasion if they failed to capitulate.

As the mists of autumn mantled the landscape, Tara became once more the focal point for parties, and gaiety abounded as if of old. Motor-car cavalcades cruised up to the front portals of the lovely house and Carla's guests had become accustomed to Mr O'Mara's bare arse and mouthfuls of grass.

It was during a charity ball that Red Butler entered her life again. It was a wonderful party and even the morose Melanie entered into the spirit of the thing, despite the fact that Ashton Whelks had gatecrashed, dressed as a Bunny Girl. The small orchestra was playing hot gospel numbers in the minstrel's gallery, and the flushed faces of the guests indicated that the drinks were going down well. At that precise moment, Red Butler strode into the ballroom. On his arm was a raven-haired sultry woman, a notorious bawdy-house madam. Carla's temper flared and her beauty was enhanced by her wrath. Mixed with her anger was a stab of jealousy, although she would never have admitted it to a living soul. Red Butler was handsome and dressed in well-cut finery. His lips were pursed in a drooped quirk of amusement as he saw Carla glowering at him and his escort. Many women dancing around the floor could not take their eyes off Red Butler, and this only served to increase the jealousy in Carla's heart. She was about to stride over and tell him in no uncertain terms that he was not welcome, when sweet Melanie trotted over to him and kissed him on the cheek. Distinctly, Carla heard Melanie say above the music, 'How wonderful it is to see you once more, dear Mr Butler. Carla will be pleased, I know she will!'

Carla was livid and stormed off to the lavatory. As the night wore on, she avoided contact with Red Butler and he, in turn, didn't seem too bothered about her attitude. Oddly enough, it was the sultry bawdy-house madam who had arrived with Butler who buttonholed Carla first.

She watched Carla shooting crows with an airgun on the back verandah, and swayed over to her as she was reloading. 'Miss O'Mara,' she said in a seductive tone. 'I know that I'm not welcome here, but let me put you straight on one thing. I am not Red Butler's lover. . . Oh, I admit, I would like to be – he's my kind of man – but, frankly, you are the one he wants.' She paused, and started rolling a cigarette in her left fingers. 'Red and I are in business together and that is all, believe me.'

Carla tossed her adorable red hair and snorted. 'Business? You call owning a brothel *business*? Fiddle-de-de.' The woman flinched. 'Morality, hey? Is that it, Miss

O'Mara?' She went on, 'Seems to me that to give lonely men a few minutes of pleasure is hardly a sin, and apart from that, we're exempt from VAT.'

Carla was so incensed that she fired the airgun at the woman. The pellet went through her ear. The woman merely smiled and said bitingly, 'Thanks, I've always wanted my ears pierced.' Carla blew a hole in the other ear, threw down the weapon, and ran into the garden to talk to her father in the box.

Carla sobbed and sobbed as her father belched on the leg of cow. So great was her grief that she forgot to hand her father the mustard and she did not hear the approach of Red Butler.

'What's the matter, Carla,' Is it that my presence wakes the dormant feeling you have for me?' said Butler softly.

Carla didn't answer. 'My God,' she thought, 'the arrogance of the swine.' She was about to tell him to go to hell, then she thought, 'No, I'll make him pay. I've lost Ashton to a music-hall turn. My life is in ruins, so revenge will be mine.'

She stood up and faced Red Butler, and to his intense astonishment threw herself into his arms and cried on his shoulder. 'Oh, Albert – I mean Red – I cannot hold my emotions at bay any longer. I truly love you.'

Butler's jaw dropped open at her words. 'Carla, my darling, I have waited impatiently for those words,' he breathed. Butler lunged forward to kiss her, but Carla turned her head away and put her hand up as if to protect herself. Her right-hand index finger went up Butler's nose and, as he bellowed in agony, Carla skipped away behind a clump of dwarf gladioli and she shouted to Red Butler, 'I love you my dearest.' Butler forgot the pain to his injured nostril, and his loins ached to possess her.

From that time on, Carla played Butler as if he were a fish on a hook. She tantalized him with glimpses of her thighs; she would cast saucy glances at him then run away and hide in the shrubbery until he got fed up looking for her and went for a McDonald's. She was a witch, a demon and Red Butler was her slave.

Meanwhile, in the North, Peabody-Brown was refusing to climb down from his tree and surrender to his generals, who were determined to get rid of the idiot and sue for an end to hostilities. Peabody-Brown's private army had been arrested and were now working for Wimpey's. Peabody was alone, but the fever of fanaticism still burned like an HP7 battery – he threw twigs at the military men and told them to, 'Go forth and multiply thy selves' – or words to that effect.

Finally, the fire brigade got him down with an extending ladder, ropes and a Mars bar. Peabody-Brown was hustled away to a prison cell and was closely guarded day and night. He was out of power, but the generals still had to find a way to parley an honourable truce. How could it be done? They had nothing to bargain with, and London knew this only too well.

It was Major-General 'Don't Give A Shit' Arkwright who came up with a suggestion: hire Red Butler to do the negotiations. His idea was greeted with enthusiasm, and preparations were made to send an envoy to see Butler.

'This Butler chap,' muttered General Ramsbottom, 'what do we know of him?' Immediately, his aide-de-camp brought in a dossier on the enigmatic Albert

'Red' Butler. The General began to peruse its contents carefully.

ALBERT BUTLER

Date of birth: Unknown
Place of birth: Unknown
Nothing known about Albert Butler's early years.
Identity of mother: Unknown
Identity of father: Unknown
First information regarding subject gleaned from log of the steamship *SS Moonglow*. Subject worked as a stoker for six months, then jumped ship at Cape Town. No further information available until recent events during the Civil War brought him into prominence.

'Odd. . . damned odd,' mused General Ramsbottom as he picked at the bones of his tandoori fried chicken. 'Just who the hell is this Red Butler?' He spoke his thoughts out loud. Butler was indeed a mystery worthy of a Sherlock Holmes investigation. Had Red Butler seen the confusion created by his dossier, he would have smiled; for there was no Red Butler other than a name on a forgotten grave in Cape Town.

The present Albert 'Red' Butler had been born Arnold Postlewaithe in the small, frequently damp, township of Oswaldtwistle in Lancashire. His mother, Ada, had been affectionately known as the 'Oswaldtwistle Bike,' mainly because half the male population had ridden her. Rumour had it that, during the Second World War, she'd had more troops that Eisenhower. Some said that you couldn't get in her bedroom for gum wrappers.

Ada Postlewaithe, despite her amorous track record, was not by a long chalk an attractive woman; she was so fat that when she passed her handbag from one hand to another, she threw it. She once cancelled an order for three pairs of knickers and two cotton mills had to close down. Ada stood only four foot five inches, and every time she hitched her corsets up she blindfolded herself. Yet men desired her and showered her with gifts in the hope of gaining her favours.

The one man she fell in love with was a forlorn soldier in the Royal Engineers called Bert Postlewaithe. His job was to look for deserters on the Rhine; the trouble was that when he found them he ran off with them. He was court-martialled in Hanover and was sentenced to three years in a military prison and a dishonourable discharge. Ada was frantic when the doctor told her she was pregnant; she had thought she was going to the surgery to have a boil lanced. What was she to do? The war was over, her lover was in prison and she was in the family way.

Things went from bad to worse for Ada until financially she was at rock bottom; she was evicted from her terraced house and her furniture thrown into the streets so often that she had the loose covers made to match the pavements. Nine months later, she gave birth to a lusty-lunged baby boy in a Salvation Army hostel for destitute women. There was only one thing for her to do: have the child adopted, and this she did. The baby was taken away and Ada took up mud-wrestling and modelling for car batteries.

Young Arnold grew up in a comfortable environment. His new parents went under the name of Catchpole but, because of their devotion to the Word of God, called themselves Mary and Joseph Gabriel. Thus Arnold Postlewaithe became Angel Gabriel. At school in the East End of London, and with a name like Angel Gabriel, young Arnold had to endure taunts from his classmates, and he swiftly had to learn how to fight. He also learned to hate religion, and became an atheist but gave it up when he realized he was getting no holidays.

The Gabriels decided to become missionaries and took the boy to the Amazon Basin where they opened a vegetarian shop in the hope of weaning hostile Indians in the Matto Grosso jungle from cannibalism. Ignoring all advice, they set off deep into the jungle with packets of nut fritters to win over the Indians, but at least had the common sense to leave their adopted son with friends.

The boy, now aged ten summers, waved his parents off, hid his Bible and commenced to read the Kama Sutra with relish. His parents never returned home. Federal troops scoured the Matto Grosso, but all they found was a waistcoat, several bones and a strong smell of chutney.

Other missionaries acclaimed them as Christian heroes, and one elderly priest remarked, 'By eating the Gabriels the savages now have the spirit of Jesus in every motion.' Arnold didn't fancy staying on at the mission now that his adopted parents had finished up a three-course meal, and so the sturdy youngster stole away into the night.

Friendly natives assisted him to make his way down the Amazon to a mining camp, where he met a tin miner and his wife who instantly took to him. Arnold thought at first that they were both suffering from yellow jaundice; then he found out they were Japanese. The kindly oriental couple had difficulty in pronouncing

'Gabriel' and 'Postlewaithe' gave them problems with breathing, so they called the lad simply 'Datsun'. He soon got fed up with that name, because people kept asking him for spares.

The Japanese wanderers took Arnold to Rio de Janeiro, and within forty-eight hours of their arrival in that exotic city, the Jap and his wife were taken into custody, accused of armed robbery and the theft of an Aztec parchment from a museum. Young Arnold was stunned by this turn of events; his little friends had a track record of crimes committed thoughout South America. They had both spent so much time in various prisons that whenever they did go straight for a time, prison governors missed them so much they asked them go back part-time. Indeed, Arnold discovered with bitterness, the Japs were hired as consultants when a new gaol was built.

Arnold was alone again at the tender age of twelve, in an uncaring metropolis. He went to visit the Japanese couple at their behest; he needed to see them urgently too. The federal authorities had placed him in an orphanage until a decision could be made regarding his future. The orphanage was a brutal institution and Arnold had no intention of remaining there, but he needed money and the only people he could turn to were the wily oriental desperadoes.

Arnold was hustled into a long narrow room with strong wire festooned down its length. He sat on a hard backless chair and waited for the Japanese man to be brought into the room. They faced each other, and a guard sat attentively close by. 'How are you, Datsun my bloy?' the Jap criminal hissed.

Arnold gestured that he was all right and poured out

his need for some money. The Jap listened impassively,
then craned his neck closer to the wire. 'Okay, my
bloy, there is slome money allight? You listlen pletty
damned glood.' He paused for a second, then hissed
again, 'You glo to house of Whistling Bamboo and ask
flor man he called Albert Butler, him friend. He give you
sometin.'

The interview was over and, thoughtfully, young
Arnold left the room. He easily gave the orphanage
teacher who'd taken him to the gaol the slip outside
the gates, and he ran like the wind, ignoring the shrill
warning from the teacher's whistle. He was a fugitive
now.

It took him a week to find the Whistling Bamboo. It
turned out to be a slum, used by oriental seaman for the
taking of a pipe of opium.

Albert Butler was a fat, coarse, bearded man in a
filthy vest and ragged trousers. He ran the place and
the prostitutes, with a Chinese partner who took care
of the opium trade.

'Jeeze, kid.' He spoke in a strong Irish accent. 'I
thought you'd be a man, bejabbers.' He commenced
to play 'Danny Boy' on a musical saw. After taking
an encore from a blowsy woman in a crêpe hat, Butler
ushered Arnold into a small office, opened a safe and
withdrew a flat metal box.

'Dis is all dey left me, son,' he chirped and then sang
'When Irish Eyes Are Smiling'.

Arnold was invited to stay with Butler and, as he had
nowhere else to go, he agreed to stay on and do odd
jobs around the place. He was given a small bedroom,
and the first thing he did was to hide the metal box
under the floorboards. Something warned him not to

trust the Irishman; and not only that, he was a rotten singer.

The next two years of Arnold's life sped by and many things happened to him. He lost his virginity at the age of fifteen to a dusky lady from Java who saw the lad in the shower one night and thought that Butler had brought a donkey into the Whistling Bamboo.

Granted, Arnold had filled out into a finely-built youth, but even Nature had been too generous in a certain anatomical region of Arnold's body. The dusky lady's eyes resembled chapel hat-pegs when she saw the lad's full-frontal bits. She tried to keep her discovery a secret for her own satisfaction on humid nights, but after a few drinks she carelessly compared Arnold's appendage to a roll of lino, and Butler's other ladies lost no time in finding out for themselves.

For the youngster it was a period of heavenly sensuality and frequent trips to a specialist in venereal problems. The sleazy world he inhabited taught him survival; he became an adept with a knife and gun, and even Butler learnt to respect the lad's prowess.

When Arnold had opened the flat metal box that the Japanese couple had entrusted to Butler for him, he had been quite disappointed to discover that the contents were only three hundred American dollars, a lapsed library card, a set of ivory buttons and a collar stud. The dollars had of course come in handy at the time, but he put the box and the rest of its contents on one side and forgot them, until one night he saw Butler holding it in his hands and perusing the case carefully.

Arnold waited until Butler had left his bedroom, and then examined the box himself. For the life of him he couldn't imagine what Butler was looking for and, impatiently, he threw the box on the floor. It clattered against the iron leg of the bedstead, there was a faint metallic ping, and the bottom of the box dropped off. Inside the cavity Arnold saw what appeared to be a piece of chamois leather. Then he realized what he was holding: the missing parchment! A noise caused Arnold to swivel his head towards the door: Butler stood there holding a gun in one hand and a wooden club in the other. 'I'll be takin' that parchment now I'll be thinkin',' he said with a bountiful smile.

Arnold had to act fast. He took up a karate stance and shouted, 'Sing "Sweet Rose Of Tralee", Red.'

Butler dropped the gun and the club and commenced to sing the song. Arnold picked up the weapons, waited until Butler had finished the song then tied him up.

Late in the night, although neither had any trust for the other, a bargain was struck between them. If the parchment was indeed a genuine map of the Aztec silver mine, they would split anything found fifty-fifty, and Arnold would get Butler an an audition for the London Palladium.

Three weeks later, with pack mules, hired guides, a crate of Guinness and a change of vest, the two of them set off for an area that lay at the foothills near the Peruvian border. The dense region of jungle and swamp was known as the 'Mukki.' Butler had a friend, Mooney, who eked out a living there making National Health moccasins for Indians with bunions. Rumour had it that Mooney had never lived anywhere else but Mukki, hence the expression: 'Where There's Mukki,

There's Mooney' (It was a pretty rotten pun, actually, but there wasn't much else to do there of a night except getting overheated with fantasies about Lillian Gish.)
Arnold kept a diary of the nightmare trip.

Monday	God; the heat, the flies, hostile natives, yet on we must go. Lost a mule this day and two of our bearers found a cat being sick in a thicket. Toilet facilities are nil, and I have a strong smell of danger.
Tuesday	Red Butler has started singing 'My Yiddisher Mama', and the guides are trying to strangle him with creepers. The going is painfully slow; we are often lost in the thick matted undergrowth and I've lost my watercress sandwiches.
Wednesday	Half-day closing.

No one will ever know just how and when they stumbled across the legendary mine, but one thing is sure: thirteen months later, Arnold Postlewaithe and Albert 'Red' Butler re-emerged from the green hell in a reconditioned Bentley, a set of top hat and tails each, and an open invitation to open an Ideal Homes Exhibition in Lima.

They had found riches beyond their wildest dreams, but avarice reached out its tendrils of desire. One night, Butler had young Arnold beaten up by paid thugs and left for dead outside the Whistling Bamboo. Butler took Arnold's share of the treasure and, that very night, left South America on a schooner after bribing the captain with ingots of silver and a promise not to sing.

Poor Arnold, close to the Grim Reaper, slowly recovered from his beating with the help of the dusky lady and her chums from the Whistling Bamboo and in return, gave the gals a permanent smile.

It didn't take long for Arnold to find out where Butler had gone: South Africa, and the hulking youth did not hesitate to go after the swine who had so wronged him.

He got a job as a deckhand on a vile ship that carried cargoes of pig iron and tin. The ship was naught but a rust bucket and should have been sunk years before. Arnold knew what hell was really like aboard that hulk: fist fights and killings were so commonplace, that at the finish, only he, the captain and four other sailors were left, and two of them couldn't play bridge. It was a maritime nightmare, and twice the captain tried to make love to him.

The ship was supposed to take on provisions at Cape Town then sail for Madras, but as soon as they docked at Cape Town, Arnold was over the side and off. He never looked back as he crept silently from the ship, first throwing away the engagement ring the captain had placed on his finger. Revenge was in his heart.

He knew that to find Butler all he had to was find a pub with a singing licence. His hunch was correct. In a smoky inn, he saw Red Butler, now going under the name of the Great Silvero, getting the bird from an audience of Boer theatrical agents.

Arnold waited outside in the dark as the concert ended and Butler was thrown into the street by a music-lover. He thrust a gun at Butler and held it to him, calling out to the Irish villain, 'Sing, you bastard, sing. . .'

Butler sang 'Daisy Daisy Give Me Your Answer Do'

followed by 'Sweet Molly Malone' before confessing where he'd hidden the fortune he'd stolen.

Arnold was unmoved, and made Butler sing 'On The Road To Mandalay' three times, then stood back as Butler was attacked by a group of members of the Noise Abatement Society. Hurled into the turgid waters that lapped the dockside, even then Butler would have survived, had he not filled his lungs with water whilst taking a last breath of air to sing the aria from 'Tosca'.

So perished the black-hearted Butler. Arnold had him buried on the cheap, took the man's name as his own, and recovered the cache of silver.

A legend was born.

Lancashire and Yorkshire, the last two counties in the Confederate Union, reluctantly retreated from every-where else in the country, withdrew behind their lines, and prepared for the inevitable invasion by the South.

Conditions were bad; no petrol for the few tanks they had bought from an dealer in Jersey; no shells left in the Bolton arsenal and only two bullets per soldier. Northern breweries had no bitter beer left and mutiny was in the air after the announcement that meat pie and chips would be on ration.

People who hoarded quantities of mushy peas could be faced with a fine or a season ticket to watch Manchester City play at home. Peabody-Brown finally went com-pletely off his chump and changed his name to Mavis. If all that wasn't bad enough, General Lee's army had reached Wilmslow in Cheshire, and General Philip Sheridan, the Woking dentist, commanding a vast con-script army from Sussex, had captured two thousand

Pen sketch of the infamous 'Masked Albert' the Barcelona baths attendant who betrayed Newcastle to the Southern Army by buying shares in a London-based brewery then flooding the pubs in the North East with the rotten stuff, knowing full well that London beer does'nt make you drunk it gives you the bends. 'Masked Albert' was captured in a holiday camp and, after the war, he was rehoused in Leeds. . .he is still appealing against the sentence. (*Sketch drawn by Albert himself through a mirror in a caravan; his wife had gone to the shops*)

Rochdale infantrymen in a pincer movement, and was poised to invade Yorkshire with long-range guns and an ample supply of dentures and gold fillings for anyone who booked a holiday in Bognor.

Heavy fighting was reported in Stalybridge when paratroopers from Camden Town clashed with paratroopers from Bradford and hand-to-hand battles took place over who should have the parking meters first. At this point in the crisis, the military junta governing the Union stopped all tea breaks in the trenches during enemy attacks, and quite a few Northern troops went on strike, took a taxi home and did some decorating.

The weather had worsened. It was so cold, brass monkeys were out lagging one another. Fuel was in scant supply. In some Northern homes, householders were burning the wooden staircases and people in bungalows had their own problems. Morale was at an all-time low as the relentless, albeit slow, advance of the Southern armies continued.

Red Butler flew to Halifax for a secret meeting with the anxious junta: they knew the cause was lost, all that they sought now was an honourable settlement and the potholes in the M6 to be filled in. Butler was greeted as a saviour when he arrived for the summit meeting, and the chant went up: 'He's all reet is Red.' Naturally enough, he became known as 'Reet' Butler.

Butler was given a twenty-one gun salute, which he admitted was flattering, though privately he rather wished they'd waited until the plane had landed. A worried knot of military men surrounded him and he was hustled away in a commandeered Morris Oxford to Halifax Town Hall for a top-level meeting and to open a poodle parlour. The streets were crammed with white-faced Yorkshire folk, peering at Butler with fervent hope in every facial crease, and twice he was offered a Woodbine.

Butler sensed the despair in his hosts; he felt their anguish at the situation, and instinctively he knew that his best bet lay in the Southern cause. As he munched his bag of chips in the car, Butler parried anxious questions about Southern stratagem and borrowed the vinegar bottle from a general.

The meeting held that early evening was the final confirmation to Red Butler that the Northern rebel government could be of little benefit to his ambitions

for supreme power; the chances of success for the North
were about as promising as getting the Pope to have a
drink in Raymond's Revue Bar.

As the meeting wore on, Butler found himself wishing
he was back in the South, even though it was a better
bitter in Halifax. A waiter came across to see if Butler
would have a dance with the mayor's wife after the
raffle, and as he bent closer in order to hear Butler's
reply, he whispered: 'Message from London, sir, there's
fifty thousand pounds in a Swiss bank for you, plus a
ticket to see *Phantom Of The Opera*, if you can create
more dissension amongst the rebels.'

Butler took a deep breath; a ticket for *Phantom Of
The Opera* surely meant that he, Red Butler, was held
in the highest esteem: treachery was the plan now. As
he thanked the waiter, he smelled a familiar perfume
and his heart lurched . . . Only one person he knew
wore that perfume – Fifi La Tour, the French stripper
and cabaret magician, whose father, Mr Ginsberg, made
tennis shorts in the East End.

'Meet me after the bar closes,' the waiter whispered.
'I'll be under the Town Hall clock.'

The words allowed Butler to recognize the voice; it
had to be Fifi.

He was transported back to the wild nights spent in
Chipping Sodbury with Fifi years ago. She had caught his
attention at a charity frog race with her high intelligence,
poise, charm and her big arse. If the Civil War hadn't
begun, Butler had always thought that he and Fifi might
have got together and opened a garage. Now, after all
this time, she had come back into his life and he made
an excuse to leave the meeting after jitterbugging with
the mayor's wife, Edna, who had a goitre.

Swiftly he made his way to the Town Hall clock. She was there, still dressed as a waiter, lounging against a lamppost, knitting a sweater. He sidled up to her. 'Fifi, what on earth are you doing here, my love?' he breathed into her ear.

She smiled a crooked smile and replied, 'Like you, Red, working for the South against these barbarians.' The story she unfolded was one of horror.

Before the Civil War had commenced she had been booked to play some Working Men's Clubs in Yorkshire and she had found, to her cost, that her East End accent had been a liability on stage. The case-hardened Northern customers hooted at her, jeered at her and when she had finally stood nude on the podium, they had shouted 'We've seen more fat on a cold chip.' Then she had been thrown out of her digs because the ignorant landlady wouldn't allow Fifi's pet alligator to play in the kitchen.

Alone and penniless, she fell for the charms of a Leeds gangster who treated her badly before going out to do a smash-and-grab at a jeweller's shop. He never returned; she found out later that he had been arrested for stealing the brick he intended to throw at the window. Her simmering hatred for all things Northern sent her scurrying to proffer her services for the Southern Cause. As she wept, Butler held her closely and kissed her gently, ignoring the matted terrier peeing up the lamppost against his leg.

'Don't worry, my darling, I'll find a way to avenge the wrongs they've done you,' he said softly as he felt her bum. Fifi smiled through her tears and, as a token of what they had once meant to each other, squeezed a blackhead on his nose.

'Goodbye, dear Red,' she whispered and, picking up her tray of drinks, she went back into the Town Hall, leaving Butler vowing to break up the Lancashire-Yorkshire union.

Fate played into Butler's hands. A Lancashire comedian on a radio talent show made a poor joke about Geoff Boycott's cricketing ability and the highly-strung Yorkshire folk, who had often slept through one of his innings, took the jest all wrong and out of context, and two Leeds commandos attempted to blow up Blackpool Tower.

The two counties glared at one another, and all the old peevishness associated with the Wars Of The Roses started up again. It was Reet Butler's chance to split the Union and leave Lancashire to go it alone. London sent in experts and civil servants with gunny sacks full of money and, as no Yorkshireman can resist brass, Yorkshire rejoined the rest of Britain and the cast of 'Emmerdale' gave out jars of potted meat at a Sheffield rally to help build a wall down the Pennines.

Butler returned to the South and Vera Lynn sang to him on a bus. Carla appeared to be glad to see him and, when Butler asked her to become his wife, she readily agreed to do so. But as they embraced her face was creased with malice.

Almost feverishly, Tara was prepared for the reception of the forthcoming marriage which had sent Henley-on-Thames spinning with anticipation. To many romantically inclined people, it was the love story of the age: the beautiful wild Carla and the bold handsome Red or Reet Butler, depending on your viewpoint, had captured the hearts of war-torn Britain.

Carla shopped in Bond Street for her trousseau and the wedding ring came from Cartier's in Paris. London was London once more; Buckingham Palace had clean net curtains up at the windows and Philip had sprained his foot playing polo again.

There was little evidence of the Civil War, apart from some tattered posters hanging from trees down the Mall. The majestic old metropolis was a blaze of colour with Yanks in their kilts and the Japanese in their flat caps, now joined by sturdy Yorkshire-born people wearing Union Jack waistcoats and offering full board in Robin Hood's Bay. There was a buoyancy in the air and smiles wreathed the faces of passers-by. The war was over, Lancashire could go to hell, that was the prevalent attitude of the hour, and mortgage rates came down. All Britain was prospering with American money, Japanese money and the Arabs felt out of it a bit. Only Lancashire stood alone and poverty-stricken, but there was never a word about a surrender. As one stout Lancastrian Bishop was heard to say: 'It's not the size that attracts the flies, it's the gyppo round the rim.' Nobody ever knew what it meant but it became a sort of anthem for beleaguered Lancashire. Yet, alone though the county surely was, there was no desire to give up the idea of a separate governing body for the North. In fact, the determination to carry on the struggle was strengthened by the complete indifference of the rest of the nation. Though it was commonplace for coachloads of holiday-makers to drive along the Lancashire border and hurl abuse at the residents behind the barricades, as far as the House of Commons was concerned, Lancashire did not exist – and wouldn't do until its people stopped messing about.

They say that in times of peril a man will rise to show the way to freedom; such a man emerged from the small town of Darwen. Culpepper Midden had lived on the hills above the town as a semi-recluse, coming into civilization only for his Social Security cheque and a pound of cooked ham from the Co-op.

He was a most imposing figure, standing well over six feet two inches on a warm day, though thin to an extreme: in fact, when he pulled his tongue out he looked like a zip. But he had a magnetic quality and, when he spoke, people listened, despite the fact that his cleft palate made it difficult to understand every intonation. Midden wore a simple toga, of home-spun appearance, and rope sandals, and was never seen without his gnarled staff. To the average Lancastrian he became a Messiah, a prophet to march them into glory – they would have to march, the trains were on strike.

There were those who actively disliked him. His ex-wife Nellie told a reporter that he was so lazy, he once fell asleep whilst running after a bus. His brother Alf snorted that Culpepper, 'Were nowt but a bloody dreamer, an' he used to cheat at Monopoly.'

Midden would walk for miles with his faithful band of intimates, and at every stop the crowd increased in size.

Culpepper Midden formed an inner cabinet of Lancashire intellectuals and, at a meeting held in camera in Manchester Town Hall, he outlined his plans for Lancashire's survival – plans that stunned his cabinet members. The main driving force of the plan centred around a rather rare weed, found only on the hills above Bolton. For many years farmers had noticed that when sheep ingested the weed they seemed to lose all interest in sex, and even the naughtiest of rams tended to droop a bit and trot away fed up.

Midden's idea was to have the weed distilled into a liquid, smuggle it down into the South, and contaminate the water supplies with the stuff. Midden argued that, in time, an impotent nation would have to turn to Lancashire for assistance. Why? Because the only antidote against the weed was, of all things, the common-or-garden Bury Black Pudding. It appeared that the pig's blood used in the puddings had the effect of nullifying the impotence caused by the plant.

That meeting was one of the most dramatic ever seen in the Town Hall. The only incident that slightly tarnished the solemnity of the occasion was when one cabinet member, under the influence of Newcastle Brown, asked if there was a weed that could make his missis randy – then wet his pants.

It was a long and arduous task, wrenching the dark mottled purple plant from the slopes of the towering hills; it rained incessantly and the hands of the men were torn and bleeding when their day's toil had ended. In Manchester University laboratories the weed was processed, the deadly sap drained from it and poured into slender glass phials. From there, the bottles found themselves secreted in body-belts around the waistbands of long johns, and the agents selected to carry the drug in their underwear then crept into the night to do their task. The men chosen were all in their late eighties and had been hand-picked for their ability to speak Cockney and Southern dialects; none of them had risen to the occasion for years, so should one of the bottles break

accidently in their underpants and the stuff get on to
their unmentionables, it would be of no consequence.

Reservoirs were naturally the first targets, but mineral
waters containing the substance were bottled in Liverpool, and despatched to the South under the label 'Sweet
Avon Water'. Meanwhile, Lancashire conscripted its
young men for the army that one day would sally forth
to victory.

There was no shortage of aspirants for the Lancashire
Army. In every public house, chip shop and pigeon
fancier's club, young males and old males laid down
their darts for their county.

Brass bands played in the parks and nubile young
Lancashire lasses in all-cotton bloomers and matching
hats gave their favours freely to the long winding queues
of would-be conscripts outside town halls all over the
shire. Old men wearing waistcoats sagging with medals
cast longing glances at the performances taking place
on the grass parklands or pavements, and the sale of
Phyllosan rocketed amongst the middle-aged.

The weaknesses of their enemies were carefully studied; the well-known Yorkshire penchant for money was
an obvious one, and so thousands of five-pence pieces
were collected in readiness to be showered on to the
streets of Leeds and Sheffield, Bradford and Halifax, to
keep the population in those areas permanently on their
knees picking them up. There was little fear of Scotland
mounting an invasion, but plans were laid for such a
contingency. Hundreds of Jimmy Shand records would
be wired up to loudspeakers strung across the border
and if the Scots tried to invade, the move could be
stopped simply by playing the records and letting the
Scots exhaust themselves by dancing reels.

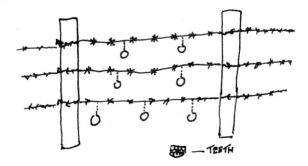

Pen sketch by courtesy of Florence Bott, showing a section of barbed wire with fried prawn balls hanging from the strands. This inhuman device was used to attract snipers who fancied a take-away supper before an invasion. Outlawed by the Geneva Convention, this device was still being used when Todmorden fell after an outbreak of anthrax in a betting shop. When the unwary sniper nibbled the prawn balls, the barbed bits on the wire hooked his dentures out and left him gnashing his gums and looking rather ridiculous.

Food supplies were garnered for the coming conflict. Yards of tripe were laid on stacker trucks in disused warehouses and clusters of black puddings and stewing steak could be clearly seen festooned from mill chimneys. Bin-liners bulged with pig's trotters and cow-heel in every branch of Woolworth's and an effigy of Edwina Curry was burnt publicly in a Clitheroe dripping-fat kiln.

Hopes were high in those wonderful days despite the fact that Manchester City football club was now in the Fourth Division. Captured London soldiers were forced to teach Cockney to the Lancastrians; if they refused to do so, they were threatened with a week's holiday in Morecambe.

All over the county, open-mouthed children sat en-
thralled as their schoolteachers extolled the virtues of
being born a Lancastrian. Hushed classrooms heard
stirring tales of valour: of how the Lancashire Fusiliers
won seven VCs before breakfast during the First World
War . . . They relived the passion and the emotion of the
Manchester Bantams who suddenly found themselves
facing the Prussian Guards on the Somme, and they
cried at the memory of the Peterloo Massacre.

On every wall in every street, faded photographs of
famous Lancastrians had been enlarged and pasted on
hoardings; Frank Randle and his toothless grimace;
Robb Wilton with finger on lip, and Ken Dodd and
his tickling stick. George Formby's old films were re-
issued on video and Gracie Fields became a cult figure
to skinheads. Cyril Smith donated his trousers to Oxfam
and they were used most gratefully as temporary housing
for ex-Borstal orphans.

The spirit of Lancashire had never been higher, and
terrible stories of Southern brutality fanned the flames
of patriotism. Small tots were told of how the awful
Southern parents never allowed their children to eat
meat pie and chips for supper, nor guzzle lemonade
during din-dins. Strong men visibly paled when informed
that a pint of bitter beer could cost twice as much in the
West End as it did say in the Rossendale Valley, and it
wasn't even strong enough to create migraine. Northern
ladies gasped when shown price labels taken from
knickers stolen in Selfridge's, knickers so diminutive
they scarcely covered their indignation.

Several peculiar groups went about saying that they
had evidence to suggest that John the Baptist had once
lived in Southport with his mother and that Moses had

meant Lancashire when he chatted about the Promised Land, though his map-reading had been so bad they'd finished up with nowt but sand. The absurdity of the themes didn't matter a jot; they served only to instil fervour into the people as the war drew towards a dreadful conclusion.

THE WITHERING VINES

'Was it not? If it truly was then was it ours?
There was a time, was there not?
When we thought it was, it was of that time wasn't
    it?
Was there ever that? Gone it was and never was, was
    it?'

(Extract from a speech by Florence Bott)

Carla postponed her marriage to Red Butler on three
occasions. It mattered little to her that the postponements
created a furore amongst her intimate circle of friends;
she explained nothing to anybody as to why she acted
in this indifferent manner but confided her innermost
thoughts only to her father in the box.

Carla would squat for hours with the box lid open
and talk to her daddy as he gargled with engine oil. Old
Mr O'Mara was supremely happy as a lawn-mower,
and often ventured now into neighbouring gardens to
prune privets with his teeth. To her parent Carla bared

115

her soul, told him of her hatred of Red Butler, of her frustration at seeing Ashton Whelks and his ventriloquist lover flaunting themselves at Beetle drives. To her precious daddy she scoffed at the ailing Melanie and her blubbering offspring. Carla's heart was of stone.

Red Butler was confused and angry at Carla's attitude: he was hailed in the South as the century's greatest man, for had he not singlehandedly destroyed the Northern Union? Butler was showered with accolades; he was awarded the OBE and the MBE, and he had unlimited credit in every Do-It-Yourself shop in Essex.

The stormy romance had to find a conclusion and, as Butler sipped his Scotch and Sweet Avon Water, he decided to put an ultimatum to Carla: either the wedding took place in a month, or he would wash his hands of her for ever. For the moment he dismissed the problem from his mind as he mulled over the odd goings-on reported in the newspapers. Several elderly men had been spotted tottering about the South at various reservoirs, and doing something peculiar in the water. When vigilant officers called upon them to explain their actions, the geriatics had taken deep breaths and vanished under the surface, never to be seen again. The newspapers also ran a series on the high divorce rate that was afflicting the South and, in the business columns, speculation was rife as to the booming success story of the company which was marketing Sweet Avon Water.

Butler had an uneasy feeling that the events reported were linked in some way. From his agents in Lancashire he knew that resistance was stiffening against any suggestion of surrender; repeatedly, he had called for an all-out drive to subdue the Lancastrians and tow them back to the national government. Alas, Whitehall's

theory that to ignore the Lancashire idiots would event-
ually bring their regime down was the accepted doctrine,
and any suggestion of a military action was greeted with
horror.

Red Butler knew the Lancashire folk better than
anybody else; it would be no easy task to break the
spirit of a people who could endure the discomforts of
a Southport boarding house in early June. Who, in their
right minds, would essay to overcome a populace who
would doggedly sit on a rain-soaked beach at Cleveleys
with a kiss-me-quick hat on and a jug of tea? No
Whitehall blimp could understand the mental strength
required to gnaw through a fresh muffin crammed with
chipped potatoes; no boffin could find a reason for the
stamina needed to wade through black tripe and pig's
trotters after ten pints of Boddington's bitter. Lancashire
would not, by jingo, be brought to her knees by any form
of intimidation.

Butler knew that elite Lancastrian commandos were
still slipping over the county borders and playing merry
hell with motorway roadworks. They had placed so
many red cones on the M62 that traffic was disappearing
up its own exhaust. Yorkshire lorry-drivers talked of
their tyres being punctured by strange little men in
balaclava helmets who then sold them street maps of
Garstang. By government edict, the chaos was played
down and simply regarded as a nuisance . . . But in the
lands that lie beyond the dreaming spires of Watford,
more sinister happenings were afoot.

In West Ealing, Mrs Doreen Pilsby, a lady of quite
heavy sensuous proportions in mind and body, was
convinced that her husband, Jim, was having an affair
with another woman. The basis for her suspicion was

that her spouse was no longer able to muster an erection when she swayed naked towards him in bed. He seemed preoccupied and distant, and finally Doreen's temper flared with frustration and she throttled him with a clothes line.

Hannah Lessing cried herself to sleep in the bedroom of the small cottage she shared with her husband Fred, who worked for Dorset meals-on-wheels as a mechanic. He had always been a lusty male and Hannah had found physical bliss with him for over ten years; but now – nothing. He seemed content to sit up in bed with his mug of Marmite and the Sporting Pink. Hannah, in concert with so many other women, took to wearing black stockings and a gym slip in order to reawaken the masculine ardour, but to no avail. The instrument of passion stayed limp. It didn't take long for the authorities to piece together the truth: without exception, Southern men were impotent. But why?

Mobile clinics roamed around the central London area, giving out free ginseng capsules to sobbing men; field hospitals were set up in the Home Counties, and it became a common thing to see ranks of naked men, with white-coated orderlies on their knees peering at inert genitalia.

Masculine pride was dead and female frustration boiled over. As the birth rate slumped to an absolute zero, panic set in and Mothercare turned a lot of stores into billiard halls. Naturally enough, whoops of frenzied delight were heard in Lancashire as the news filtered through, and Midden decided to put the second part of his master plan into operation. He would send Northern lads with healthy sexual functions into the South to woo the women there. The weed had done its job only too

Novelty hat worn by certain infantrymen from Ealing. During the battle for a Winsford fish diabetic clinic, the hats were filled with a brace-rotting fluid that caused the trousers of Northern troops to drop in the heat of the skirmish. Apart from sustaining severe cramp and a chill up the what's-it, the embarrassment caused a Bolton corporal to elope with a German architect and they spent the war in a large bucket of glue until they were put away by a specialist.

well. What had emerged from the exercise was that the distilled moorland plant appeared to increase the female desire as it decreased the male fruitiness; Midden's world was his oyster and, after overpowering the South, he fully intended to carry out the same scheme in Scotland and Yorkshire.

Meanwhile, Red Butler and Carla were joined as man and wife. It was a ceremony carried out with pomp and circumstance. The rays of a fevered sun bled themselves across the Thames and threw the old church into bold relief as Butler and Carla stood at the Saxon altar and made their vows. Devastatingly beautiful in her bridal gown, Carla beamed at her handsome husband; only her eyes remained cold. Melanie wept and her child howled; Mr O'Mara's box had been put on castors so that Carla could roll him down the aisle with her, and Ashton Whelks gave his good wishes to a statue of the Virgin Mary.

The wedding reception was held at Tara, and the fine old mansion for a time regained its former sparkle as the guests danced and drank, forgetting their immediate problems for the moment. Carla had never been so radiant. The men gazed at her in awe and the ladies wept for a beauty that they themselves would never have. As the grey bars of dawn stretched into faltering light, Carla and Red Butler waved their guests into the waiting cavalcade of cars then, hand in hand, they entered the house and with trembling anticipation, slowly, and in silence, climbed the neo-Georgian staircase to the room that had been allocated as the honeymoon suite.

With a finger to her lips, Carla entered the ornate bedroom. Red Butler would have carried her over the threshold, but he'd done his back in at golf, and he was forced to wear a medical corset under his money belt. The weight ratio was such that, should he fall during the physical transit of his bride, he might well turn turtle on the carpet and remain in a most peculiar posture, so beloved in the music-hall orbit.

Swiftly Carla undressed in the darkness of the room. Butler rather noisily dismantled his attachments, and slid naked between the black silk sheets . . . It was the moment for the first move in Carla's plan for revenge. Magnificent in a sheer gossamer bra with wide-gusset peach-tinted cami-knickers with a saucy suspender belt and ebony hose, she switched on a bedside light and stood alluringly waiting for Butler to lunge for her body and drag her into a frenzy of carnal emotion. At that precise moment, Carla intended to thunder to her husband: 'You cannot have me – and you will never have me.' Then she would storm out of the house and sleep with her daddy in the box.

On went the light to reveal Butler sipping a glass of Sweet Avon Water and brandy. He looked at her, and his eyes darkened with adoration. Carla twanged one of her suspender straps and roared triumphantly, 'You cannot have me. . .' As she paused for breath, Butler yawned and said sleepily, 'Of course we won't bother, dear. It's been a long day, and we're both knackered.'

Carla's mouth dropped open. 'What the bloody hell?' she thought to herself. Butler's reputation as a randy goat was legendary; it was quite openly known that Butler would mount anything that had a pulse. As Butler snored into the tunnel of oblivion, Carla peeled back the top sheet and closely scrutinized his lower anatomy. What she saw gave her a slight attack of acid; for there, 'twixt his hair-matted legs, lay an appendage that more than resembled the valve off a tyre from a child's tricycle.

She paced the floor the entire night in a fit of wild frustration and anger; the swine! The rotter! Well, fiddle-de-de, she'd lost the first battle but the war was yet to be won. On Sunday morning she played a recording of burlesque bump-and-grind songs and waggled her attractive naked rump in Butler's swarthy face; he applauded heartily and went back to reading *Uncle Tom's Cabin*. On Sunday evening she read him extracts from *The Perfumed Garden* as she sat on his knee in just her bloomers; Butler laughed and sipped his Sweet Avon Water and invited her to play a game of draughts. She hurled her cup of Earl Grey at his head and ran off to the bedroom, sobbing with fury, and also, as she well knew in her heart of hearts, a burning desire to get a leg over.

On Monday and Tuesday, she rented an anthology of porno movies, roped him to a chair and made him sit through the lot as she bent her naked buttocks towards him. Butler merely smiled and asked for a grilled kipper. On Wednesday night, she massaged his manhood until dawn, but the droop hung on and she agreed to play 'Trivial Pursuit'. On Thursday she couldn't take any more and left the house to go on a pub crawl. In the Dog and Dagger she met a strapping young footballer but, after removing his shorts, Carla found he was worse off than Butler in that department *and* he had immature testes.

She was soon to learn that all the other women she encountered were in the same boat: sex starved and neglected. The main topic of conversation in the hairdressers' and in Tesco's was 'lack of rumpo'.

Carla spent a fortune on fresh oysters for her husband, but the only thing that stirred was his abdominal muscles when he threw up. Nothing excited him; he took to watching Australian soap operas, so Carla knew he wasn't well. Lots of men now were content to spend an evening at home with their newspapers and pipes, and women crept into toolsheds with drawings of phallic symbols and a lump of wood; the situation was desperate, to say the least, and Carla decided to use Robin Starch on Butler.

There was a terrible stench of violence in the air: in every town and city, village and hamlet of the South, predatory hordes of rampant women were attacking any male who had been foolish to wander the streets by himself. The stories that abounded were brutal and horrific. In Brighton, a retired eye specialist in a hotel bar casually remarked to a barmaid that he had something special for the ladies in his trousers. On his way to the loo, a crazed air hostess stripped him savagely, then beat him up when she discovered that the 'something special' was a charm bracelet he'd won in a raffle.

No man was safe when night fell. A taxi-driver was flagged down in Wardour Street by two lady pensioners who forced him to drive into Hyde Park then tied him to a tree, removed his trousers and took photographs of his lower torso. He was found the following morning in a state of shock with something awful daubed on his testicles and a note saying 'Things Ain't What They Used To Be'.

Businessmen took to wearing wigs and frocks in order to get to the office unmolested. Naturally enough, the economy began to suffer as overseas buyers found it increasingly difficult to deal with a tycoon who sat behind a desk with an order book and a knitting pattern. The deadly Lancashire moorland weed had indeed done its task well. The male libido was at its lowest ebb, and battered husbands started to form groups to discuss such ailments as headaches and back trouble. Many men took up karate in order to defend themselves against a possible attempted rape, even though stimulation was impossible. The pubs now were full of aggressive ladies who chatted and bragged about the sex they'd had in the past, and the landlords behind the bars tutted in distaste.

The South had indeed won a hollow victory, and rebel Lancashire pressed on with the next facet of the Master

Plan. Virile commando units infiltrated the tense South with the oddest invasion in history. Swiftly, and reeking of expensive talc, they made themselves available to eager females suffering the agonies of frustration, and relieved them with unbridled joy. The news that men had arrived who could still perform the age-old ritual spread quicker than a fat-free diet sheet, and from Penzance to Kilburn the ladies rejoiced and gave thanks.

There were some bitter fruits to taste in the carrying out of the Master Plan; many a well-endowed Lancastrian male had to be sent home exhausted and injected with vitamin E and oyster membranes. Many had been so abused in certain anatomical areas that they would have nightmares for years to come about teeth marks, especially after having the odd wee-wee.

Three lads from Morecambe, locked up in a police station for having no insurance on their jeep, were broken out of jail by a maddened crowd of day-trippers from Woking. As the day-trippers were females, they firstly nagged the police officers into a state of inertia then rushed the station and freed the lads. Happy to be released, it soon dawned on the poor chaps that they would have been better off in the nick, because they were dragged off to the Embankment and ravished. One of the Morecambe men expired due to the treatment meted out, but onlookers said that he vacated the physical world with a bountiful smile that never left his lips.

It was the moment to exercise the next part of the Plan. Within a week, the commando units were hoisted aboard a fleet of coaches and the retreat to Lancashire commenced. It was a deliberately slow progress homewards, for festooned on the rear of the coaches, in bold print, hung banners with the legend 'The Only Thing

Left Stiff In The South Is An Upper Lip . . . Come North
To Lancashire, Girls, For Lasting Satisfaction'.
It had the desired effect. From Exeter to West Ealing,
from Folkestone to Berkshire, long straggling lines of
hopeful femininity snaked northwards for the promise of
rumpo. All the motorways were impassable as the ladies
trudged and sang saucy ditties. In the War Office, the
Army Chiefs of Staff abandoned any military retaliation,
knowing full well that the refugees heading North would
hamper any tactics. Not only that, the Southern troops
were so ashamed of themselves, they were refusing to
take communal showers, and there was the ridiculous
spectacle of soldiers shoving kapok down their trousers.
Lancashire waited for the influx of crumpet with tremors
of anticipation and the scent of victory was heady.

Culpepper Midden was the new Messiah. Faultless in
his strategy, many thought; few knew there was a vital
flaw in his Master Plan.

Carla had tried everything to arouse Red Butler, but the
marriage had still not been consummated, and she was
fed up. The only comfort she could take refuge in was
the fact that every other woman was in the same boat.

She had spent hours showing him rude films and
French underwear, but all Butler seemed to want to
do was put a bet on. Carla herself had attacked other
men to see if she could have it away, but to no avail:
they either apologized and went to sleep, or cried on her
shoulder and owned up to their true golf handicap.

She spent the nights drinking whilst Butler listened to
'The Archers'. For nearly three days he had suffered
from an upset stomach, and had only drunk boiled

Symbolic wall mural: 'Black Pudding In A Fist'. Drawn by
someone with a bad leg, this sketch became the centre-piece of
the Bacup Foot and Mouth Second Cavalry standard, which
flew over the Gas Board in Rochdale during a power cut in a
Druid's tailoring shop. It was captured by Southern forces and
used as a handkerchief by a hay fever victim in Stoke Poges,
his wife hasn't been too well either. . .

milk. One night, as she was about to lurch up the
winding stairway to bed, she noticed that Red Butler
was standing naked in the study, gazing dumbly at
a dirty postcard. As the rain pounded on the gables
of Tara, Carla's hand gripped the oak newel of the
staircase. She gasped for breath and her heart drummed
as her eyes saw the miracle before her: Red Butler had
an erection.

She stumbled into the study and embraced him. He
tried to disentangle himself from her arms, but she had
a strength born of despair and he could not escape from

her embrace. He gasped as her lips sought his. 'No . . .
No . . . Carla. *No.*'

She heeded not his plea; her loins were a furnace; her
every fibre screamed for his body as she heard herself
croak, 'No, no, my dear. Not this time.' She scooped him
into her arms and started to carry him up the stairs.
Butler yelled and tore at her hair in his frenzy to
escape. Carla merely smiled a thin smile. 'It's useless,
my dear, tonight is mine,' and, with that, she mounted
the stairs to the bedroom.

As the elements howled around the house and the trees
waved in fear at the storm's fury, Carla threw her naked
husband on to the bed and slaked her thirst upon his
whimpering body. She was an animal that night and
exclaimed that if he was up to it on milk, what would
he be capable of on whipped cream?

The night sobbed into a chilled dawn over Tara, but
from the darkened chamber came no sounds other the
creaks of passion.

Lancashire was Sodom revisited. The whole county was
simply one massive orgy of uninhibited lovemaking. The
pubs stayed open all day and the tinkle of music was a
constant backcloth to the flesh-threshing that went on
outdoors and in.

So engrossed had the Lancastrians become that every-
day activity ceased. Trains didn't run, nor any other
passenger services. Many shops refused to open their
doors because customers were likely to have a leg-over
on the chest freezers. Nobody could park a car for fear of
running over a couple panting on the road, and Pontin's
became a nudist camp.

BAG of SPANNERS

A Howitzer, specially adapted for hurling black puddings and
suet crusts into enemy trenches. Invented by Len Sprigott, it
was made from an old pair of metal trousers and a pipe from
a Tudor lavatory. Note the handle on the side of the cannon.
This turned the gun up and played tunes from Radio 2. On
a good day, a black pudding could be fired to a distance of
one mile and, on impact, it uncrossed its legs and started
biting. (*Courtesy of Miss Bott's Museum of Natural Peruvian
Knickers*)

Tourism was up fifty per cent and the latest craze was
strip bingo. The Americans poured into the county and
the Newcastle Japanese had never had it so good. But
beneath the gaiety and the lust, resistance was forming
among the Lancashire women who were now feeling
the pinch – as it were. Their husbands never bothered
to come home to a meat pie and pickles any more;
all they had to do was parade in any hotel lobby,
be picked up by a Southern huntress and be sure of
liver pâté and smoked salmon in return for a gobbet of
nookie.

It couldn't last, this sexual Valhalla, and it was a Burnley woman who journeyed to London to tell of the Culpepper weed and what it had done. Meanwhile, as the menfolk grew increasingly tired, their Northern wives and sweethearts locked them in the bedrooms and, armed with kitchen utensils, started to fight their Southern sisters in pitched battles.

When scientists found out the Lancastrian secret, that pig's blood was the perfect antidote to the weed, the impotent South recovered very quickly and demanded that their womenfolk return home. The incensed ladies of Lancashire threw back the last of the randy Southlanders in one fierce encounter that had all the trademarks of a well-manicured Dunkirk and, with pinafores flying in triumph, the Northern ladies waddled back to their errant menfolk.

Culpepper Midden was alerted that, at last, the decision to invade Lancashire had been made. Already, Southern armies were advancing towards the border, bristling for revenge over drooping members.

THE ROSE STANDS ALONE

'The point of the issue is surely to point out the point
of it all? There are several points to the issue and some
are pointed ones in the unfolding drama that points to
the issue we've pointed out just now. Who's to blame?
Who can point the finger first? I think we've made the
point.'

(Extract from a speech by Florence Bott)

With Lancashire surrounded by hostile forces, it seemed
that the rebel county must surely topple under the sheer
weight of the hostile Southern forces digging in on her
borders. Yorkshire had no intention of coming to help; in
fact, the Yorkshire Cricket Club tried to buy Old Trafford
to use as a Freddy Trueman Memorial Home for retired
fast bowlers and fallen women.

Then, in the darkest hour for the Red Rose county,
capricious fate took a hand in these turbulent affairs. The
High Commissioner for Higher Education in Australia
was forcibly ejected from Stringfellow's Niterie for

drinking lager straight from the can. Watching the
wretched official perform a parabola into the street was
a Lancashire secret agent who spoke fluent cockney and
could do an impression of a wallaby. He dusted down the
sozzled Aussie and they sat on the edge of the pavement
and sang 'Waltzing Matilda'.

In the sober light of the following noon, the Australian
awoke to find that the secret agent had driven him up
the M1 in the boot of a Ford Escort, and he was now
in Culpepper Midden's emergency war room, situated in
the cellar of a blouse factory in Burnley.

Whilst the Australian shouted, 'Bloody Pommie Bas-
tards' and 'Get me another can of Foster's,' Midden curtly
demanded an explanation from the secret agent as to his
purpose in abducting the Aussie.

'Sir, please bear with me, even though my idea may
appear crazy . . .' He launched into what was to become
Lancashire's master military stroke. In simple terms, the
agent (known as 002, which meant licensed to strangle
hernias) outlined his plan: to import kangaroos and
train them to fight. When they'd been sitting on the
pavement, the Australian had talked bitterly about the
ravages caused to crops by 'the bloody roos', and how
most Aussies would like to see the back of them and
shut Rolf Harris up.

When the Aussie High Commissioner sobered up,
Culpepper, now wildly excited by the secret agent's
plan, thrashed out a deal with the official from the
Antipodes. Lancashire would buy every Australian soap
opera for peak-time viewing on Granada, plus herds of
sheep, in return for free air ferrying of kangaroos to the
beleaguered county. It was a hard bargain that was forged
that day and, as anybody knows who's sat through 'Sons

And Daughters', the Australian government had finally got its own back for being stuck with the Tolpuddle Martyrs.

Meanwhile, Southern troops had invaded West Didsbury, the Manchester suburb, and the rates shot up. There was stiff resistance to the invaders at first, but the constant replaying of a 'Singalonga Max' album during bayonet charges demoralized the defenders and wholesale desertions were reported on all fronts. The rest of the North of England and Scotland cocked a snoot at Lancashire's plight, and Culpepper Midden's impassioned speeches to give aid fell on deaf ears.

In Glasgow, the Americans were shooting a new series of 'Dallas', this time with J.R. Ewing in a kilt and sporran, and Miss Ellie was tossing the caber. On Tyneside, most Geordies wore kimonos and spats now, and their Japanese counterparts gave free pies away with every geisha massage. No, Lancashire could get knotted.

Crack London storm-troops came ashore by landing craft, and took control of Fleetwood; then took another look at it and wished they hadn't.

Cumbria rented Lake Windermere to Southern naval units and Fleet Air Arm personnel, and charged them two pounds fifty pence each for mystery coach trips to Ulverston. The 3rd Bedfordshire Light Infantry invaded Liverpool but got fed up with being mugged and retreated to Ormskirk for the Bank Holiday.

There is an old Lancashire adage which states: 'When a Lancastrian has his back to the wall . . . you'll always find whitewash on his coat'. Lancashire had her back to the wall, and defeat now seemed to stare the county in the face. Then came the first batch of kangaroos.

They were dropped by parachute into Wigan and some of them drank out of the canal. Swiftly, the animals were heaved on to waiting trucks and driven to a training camp at Leigh, where ex-boxers from a gymnasium taught the powerful creatures the art of the pugilist. There wasn't a moment to lose.

That fine old Southern General, Lee, toyed with his cheroot and watched his soldiers advance with confidence towards the enemy trenches outside the town of Clitheroe. It was a warm hazy morning as the troops commenced their attack, and Lee dreamt of the medals he'd get for his part in the Civil War. His blissful state ended abruptly when the hardened troops under his command started to run back in a blind panic. With sword raised aloft, Lee trumpeted loudly for an explanation for the apparent cowardice he had just witnessed. A white-faced sergeant juddered to a halt and panted, 'Cor blimey, sir, I fink the bloody fools have cross-bred rats with hares or somefink! Bloody monsters chasing us!'

Lee was about to smell the man's breath when, out of the corner of his eye, he saw hundreds of bouncing apparitions wearing boxing gloves and knocking seven bells out of his infantry. Open-mouthed, he hadn't time to back away from an enormous kangaroo who gave the military genius a left hook and sent the General staggering into a cess pit.

The Southern lads had no chance; from all sides the spring-heeled roos battered them into a blubbering submission and Clitheroe was saved.

Ten thousand Southern soldiers were captured that day and bags of kangaroo manure were sold at forty pence a bag to allotment holders and market gardeners.

West Didsbury surrendered under the attack of the kangaroo army, and a short-sighted spinster posted a letter in a roo's pouch. It was, dear reader, a débâcle on a grand scale. The Southern armies, punched, kicked and buffeted, fled in complete disarray, leaving their weapons on the field of battle. The world's press reported the events with glee, and a trade union official demanded that the kangaroos be given membership of the TUC.

The whole of Lancashire rejoiced; the people danced and sang and the kangaroos bounced and mated. Australian sheep came over in droves and the Aussie television drama 'The Young Doctors' knocked 'Coronation Street' out of the ratings. In London, there was a mantle of gloom over the turn of affairs, and in Wales, a rogue kangaroo raped a sheep herd by himself, and produced loin chops that could jump out of a grill pan.

It soon became obvious that there would be a serious threat to the ecology if the kangaroos kept on multiplying at the rate they seemed to be, and there was so much wool available that Culpepper Midden ordered every Lancastrian to wear two sweaters at once. The House of Commons held an emergency debate over the crisis and Black Rod was taken to hospital after being thumped in the ear by a kangaroo from the public gallery.

The kangaroos bounced into Yorkshire and one of them was signed up by Wakefield Rugby League Club. They sprang into the North-East and the Border Counties and nobody bent down in a kilt any more. Britain was the laughing-stock of Europe once again, and the Germans and the French fell about with mirth: if the kangaroos mated with the British, they said, the Common Market could be kept on the hop. This dreadful sally was widely reported and a spokesman for the SDP told a conference on effluence that, if they got elected at the next election, the kangaroo issue would be solved by simple animal vasectomy on the male of the species or shooting them on the bounce. This remark created an uproar, and the spokesman was branded as a racist and a sexist by a left-wing hothead at a meeting in a homosexual wine-bar.

Culpepper Midden was no longer the saviour of Lancashire. The kangaroos were everywhere and people were sick of eating lamb cutlets. The smell in the streets was appalling and heaps of wool, sheared from the vast rambling herds of sheep, caused problems with car back axles.

Young children started to ape the natural hopping movement of the energetic kangaroos, and it became a common sight to see tiny tots jumping up and down in playgrounds and nursery schools. By this time, the ever-increasing bands of roving kangaroos had penetrated Tyne and Wear, and the desire to copy anything vaguely Western got the better of the Japanese who took to hopping with extra-sprung shoes. Devotees of martial arts studied the agility of the roo, and instead of karate there now dawned the age of 'kangarate'. In simple terminology, an adept didn't just kick his opponents in a contest – he now jumped on them until they were sick.

A madness took over the realm; there were bouncing parties, bouncing stage shows and revues, and comedians had a new lease of life with horrid jokes such as:

'What do you get if you cross a Scotsman with a kangaroo?' Answer? 'A hop-Scotch.'

Pen sketch of the Pennine Chain in winter, with troops using a mobile lavatory run by Sister Mildred and her all-nun Ninja team. Dysentery was an ever present problem when bottled beer began to ice up in a military caravan.

'Did you hear about the woman who slept with a kangaroo? Nine months later she had a bouncing baby boy . . . the only trouble is, they can't stop it bouncing.'

Ken Dodd sang 'Love Is Like a Kangaroo', and he carried on stage a tickling pouch. A very coarse comic was hustled from a civic hall in Blackburn for saying to the audience, 'What's brown and jumps up and down? Kangaroo shit.'

The Civil War was forgotten as the kangaroo menace spread throughout the nation. The sheep still presented a nuisance but nothing on the scale that the randy roo was capable of. Dogs, cats, large hamsters, they were all fair game for the lustful marsupial, and even slow-moving nudists had been known to complain about roving paws.

Red, or Reet, Butler was in a seventh heaven. Carla was most demanding of his physical services now that the droop-drug had been destroyed, and he was content to wallow in bed, just waiting to be called upon.

Carla, on the other hand, was still burning for Ashton Whelks, and it came as a slap in the face when she saw him crouched in the pouch of a heavily-built kangaroo. 'Oh, Ashton,' she would sigh as she sat on the edge of her father's box, watching him chew the weeds from a rockery bed. 'Oh, what might have been, my darling!'

Melanie and her son never came to Tara now; the old mansion was surrounded by kangaroos and Melanie couldn't go near them because the proximity of one gave her a virulent rash.

Carla hated Butler but needed his body; her sexual appetite was a powerful one, and he satisfied her desires. She longed for the one man she couldn't have: Ashton Whelks. Part of her recoiled at the knowledge that he was unofficially engaged to the fat kangaroo, but her other, more sympathetic side, ached to smooth his fevered brow and wipe the kangaroo spittle from his bi-focals.

Meanwhile, an enterprising tourist board found that the kangaroo plague, far from deterring visitors from coming to Britain, actually helped to stimulate tourism when put over in a light-hearted manner. This sent the pound sterling higher than a giraffe's belly button. The President of the United States asked the Senate to pass a bill to import kangaroos, and so bolster the US motel trade in Florida, and in Australia the public demanded the return of their native mammal. Riot level was reached in Sydney and Brisbane, when aborigines made matters worse by wailing to some god or other and it rained for six weeks in Perth, and a sponsored boomerang-throwing at Ayers Rock went wrong when half the boomerangs failed to return after clattering against a mobile latrine. To suggest that events had become somewhat confused would be an understatement in the classic mould. The intense desire of the imported kangaroo to exercise its sexual drive had resulted in a staggering increase of little kangaroos, and the situation had now been officially declared as 'Requiring Urgent Attention.' There was no doubt about it: Britain had a plague on its hands and the smell in the streets was bloody awful. The hairy sods were everywhere – in gardens, in tool sheds, behind locked doors and snuffling in dustbins. One could not walk a hundred yards without getting a clout round the proverbial from a beaming bouncing marsupial. In London, the police were clamping kangaroos found dozing in Regent Street and, on some occasions, had recourse to arrest some of them for urinating in Hyde Park.

To further the chaos, the Southern Army had trained its own roos to box the Northern Army's pugilistic kangaroos, and so military tactics now became one ridiculous brawl. Soldiers couldn't even make a half-decent charge because they couldn't get a fair run across no man's land without tripping over a confounded kangaroo in the act of mounting its mate. To all intents and purposes the Civil War was over, because of the immensity of the kangaroo problem, and without any ceremony whatsoever an armistice was hurriedly signed before the document got covered in roo shit.

There was no emotion at the cease-fire, no tears, no joyous laughter at the realization of peace once again; nothing. It was as if the British public had been drugged and cowed by an oppressor, their spirit had gone as they ran like hell from rampant kangaroo gangs.

Resistance groups began to form: an underground web of dedicated fighters for freedom from the domination of the kangaroo, and North and South became reunited.

Australia cried 'Enough' and refused to have any more kangaroos in that country. The Americans followed suit after a union official discovered that many of the kangaroos let into Florida were not only working as bell-hops in cut-rate motels, but moonlighting as cab drivers at the airports. In short, Britain was stuck with the problem and, after the initial thrill of being carried about in a pouch, the Japanese became depressed when the kangaroos started kicking Toyotas over in car parks. They began to stream back home, taking their nice little bank balances with them.

The Russians sent three roos up into space but the blessed things kept springing up and down in the module and the space vehicle turned left at Mars and vanished into a black hole.

Nightly the resistance workers crept up on unsuspecting kangaroos, threw nets over them and put them in cages, but the kangaroo population was increasing at such a pace that these efforts were in vain. Something had to be done, and it was Culpepper Midden who found the solution: feed the kangaroos the Lancashire moorland weed. It worked. Within six weeks, the bounce had gone out of the male of the species. They would sit for hours on their tails making pitiful sounds as the females leapt about in evident frustration.

Relief swept across this sceptred isle as the kangaroo birth rate dropped, and Culpepper-Midden was handed a medal.

The will to live had gone and the male kangaroos simply pined away and were canned as cat food. The females turned to other life forms for satisfaction, and for a time there were some very peculiar chickens knocking about. The Resistance got in touch with Norway and outlined a plan to wipe out the marsupial menace once and for all. The females were loaded on to boats, landed near lemmings, persuaded to fool around with the male lemmings and, when the time came for the ritual of leaping over the cliffs into the sea, the randy girl roos followed for a spot of nookie. The plan worked better than any scientist could have hoped and, ere long, the kangaroo had disappeared from our shores.

From village to village, from township to city, church bells rang in thanksgiving and the task of cleaning up was tackled with enthusiasm.

Britain was one nation again and a better understanding had emerged from the strife. It was mooted that a replica of the House of Commons should be built in Carlisle and Wimpey's put a tender in for it. No longer would London make national decisions; for half the year all MPs would travel by coach up to Carlisle and make a bugger of things there as well.

The Royal Family insisted on spending more time in the North as a goodwill gesture, and Prince Philip put forward the proposal that a day should be set aside as a holiday and called 'National Kangaroo Day' as a remembrance that it was that creature who had welded the nation together.

The Eastern Bloc was told in no uncertain terms that any attempt at building up a nuclear warhead advantage in Europe would be met by the West's ability to infest Moscow with wallabies and sheep. Also, secretly, plans had been laid to contaminate vodka distilleries with the dreaded droop weed from Lancashire. One disturbing factor had emerged, however. Many men had become hooked on Sweet Avon Water and the stuff was being boot-legged on a large scale, in particular by disenchanted monks who'd gone off women anyway. Wives and sweethearts were actively encouraged to inform on any of their menfolk who seemed to have gone off the boil, as it were. These wretched men could then be sent to 'drying out' centres for treatment, which consisted of the intake of real ale, strip-tease shows and porno movies.

As the economy boomed, crime diminished, and out-of-work burglars and muggers were given employment in the Inland Revenue so that they could still keep their hand in with corruption. It was a brave new world in a lot of ways, but for Carla O'Mara nothing had changed.

Tara held nothing any more for Carla. Only the sweet presence of her father chewing the lawns kept her from leaving the house for ever. How she longed for the old days; the glittering parties, the ardent beaux. Her friends had gone and since the extinction of the kangaroo, it was a problem to obtain servants. Once again, as of yore, the old mansion began to fall into a state of decay.

Melanie and her offspring had left the country, and the last that Carla had heard of them was that they were doing a double act on the QE-2 with spoons and a zither. Red or Reet Butler, as he was still often referred to, loved Carla passionately, but he'd had a hip replacement and felt off colour a bit. Ashton Whelks she saw but briefly. Since his lover, the husky kangaroo, had

The vulgar hoarding erected in Preston by a Gypsy trumpet orchestra upon being told to shift by a detective. During the Civil War, it became a symbol of resistance in enemy occupied areas, and its slogan, 'Up Your Bum', was put to music and played a lot in the Gas Board.

vanished Whelks had become a recluse and torn with grief.

Carla's days were spent watching her father sharpening his dentures before tackling the weeds in the rose bushes, and her eyes would mist over as she emptied the debris from his truss.

Her life was in ashes, as were her dreams . . . every day and every night was an absolute vacuum. Even a fifty-pound win on the greyhound Derby meant nothing to her.

Butler tried hard to involve his wife in day-to-day matters of state, but her hatred had now cooled into a total indifference towards her swashbuckling husband. Because of his gammy hip he now buckled more than he swashed. They never made love any more, although Butler still desired Carla and tried nightly to woo her in the sheets. But Carla's habit of using a knitting machine in bed tended to dampen his ardour and, to make matters worse, her machine kept chipping the paint off his harp.

It was an intolerable situation, and matters came to a head when she attempted to brain Butler with a lump hammer after she had caught him cheating at Cluedo. That very night she ran out of the house and into a storm that had raged for over three days and nights. Her nightdress was sodden and the fangs of lightning threw her wild face into a bold cameo relief as she fled from the nightmare of her existence. 'Oh, Ashton,' she shrieked aloud, 'I need you.'

Sobbing and stumbling, she crashed through the shrubbery where a cat was being sick. Behind her, she heard Red Butler calling out her name, his voice faint on the edge of the wind, 'Carla, Carla!' Her lungs were burning and she threw her arms around a gnarled oak tree and paused to fight for breath.

A sound made her nerves jangle with apprehension; something or someone was approaching towards her through the matted undergrowth. Carla realized that she still had the lump hammer in her hand, and she tightened her grip on the tool and crouched behind the oak tree's trunk. At first she thought that Red Butler was coming for her, and then she caught the distinctive odour of an animal . . . Suddenly, highlighted by the streaks of fire creasing the black heavens, the bulk of a large adult kangaroo came into her vision, and Carla instinctively knew that this was the creature that Ashton had fallen in love with.

A searing rage knifed through her body. Damn this kangaroo that had caused Ashton so much pain! Strength coursed through her arm as she brought the lump hammer down on to the roo's head. The animal reeled around for a few seconds, tried a feeble hop, then dropped to the ground like a stone. Carla retched at her action, then cautiously crept nearer to the fallen animal.

The kangaroo was dead.

Carla slumped to her knees and let the bloodied lump hammer slip from her fingers as the tears came to her eyes. She knew that Ashton would never forgive her for killing his kangaroo, despite the fact that the animal had forsaken him. She had lost Ashton for ever . . .

Or had she? The germ of an idea came into her mind. She rose to her feet and commenced to pull the kangaroo by its tail back towards the house. The giant herbivorous marsupial mammal was too heavy for her and she gave up the task and ran home to get help from Red Butler.

Butler was searching for her in the thicket. She wasted no words, merely grabbing his arm and pulling him in the direction of the kangaroo's final resting place. Butler's hip was giving him some trouble and he desperately wanted to pee, but such was his love for Carla that he gritted his teeth and allowed her to drag him along.

Carla briefly and curtly told Butler what she had in mind: to get the dead animal back into the house.

'What for, my bold beauty?' lisped Butler. 'We've got enough meat in the chest freezer'

She glared at him. 'I don't want to eat the bloody thing,' she snarled. 'I want to skin it.'

Butler saw the demented look in her eyes and said not another word after excusing his action of unzipping his flies and relieving himself against a clump of thistles. Together, they tugged and heaved and slowly they dragged the kangaroo towards Tara. No words passed between them as they toiled in unison across the water-logged grounds.

Butler was puzzled as to why Carla wanted to skin the carcass but he held his tongue. The intent look on Carla's face gave evidence that she would brook no such questions.

The storm had abated and the only sound now to be heard was Carla's father playing a Jew's harp in his box. At last, the kangaroo lay in the garage and the pair stopped to get their wind back.

'This will do,' Carla panted. 'I don't need you any more tonight.'

Red Butler opened his mouth to speak, but Carla pushed him out of the garage and closed the doors behind him. Her eyes were bright and feverish as she began to skin the dead animal, and she crooned softly to herself a tune that she and Ashton had once harmonized together on stage during a concert for 'The Friends Of The Mafia's Hot Pot Supper' at the Mechanics' Institute, Rhyl. She worked swiftly and cleanly, stripping the skin from the kangaroo, and as dawn curled the first tendrils of light into the fabric of the night her work was completed.

Butler slept until the late afternoon. A strange sound had alerted him from the depths of an exhausted slumber; the sound of something hopping up the stairs. He leapt out of

bed and picked up the embossed chamber pot in readiness
to brain the intruder.

As the hopping noise neared the bedroom door, he
raised the utensil, forgetting that it was rather full. The
contents hit him full countenance just as the door opened
– and in hopped Carla, in the kangaroo skin.

Wiping his face on a soiled bandana, Butler gazed in
a stunned fashion at the sight of his wife inside the
kangaroo's pelt.

'Don't you see? Ashton will love me now! Don't you
see?'

Butler knew then, in that moment, that his wife had
gone off her chump; she was bananas.

Roaring with glee, Carla about-turned and hopped out
again – and Butler swooned.

Bouncing along the main road, Carla kept shouting
out to startled passers-by, 'Ashton will love me, wait and
see.'

Over and over again she sang the words until she
hopped to a halt outside Ashton Whelks' bungalow.
She cupped her hands to her lips and screamed, 'Ashton,
darling, come to your ever-lovin' Carla.'

The front door was thrown open and out stepped
Ashton Whelks, with a set of magnifying glasses strapped
to the end of his nose. 'Carla, Carla O'Mara, is that really
you?' He spoke in a tremulous voice.

'Oh yes, my darling, it is,' Carla said in a cracked tone,
and with that she hopped towards him.

A large crowd had gathered to witness the most
astonishing end to a love story. Carla had showered
Ashton with kisses, then pushed him into her pouch; he
had responded with enthusiasm since he thought she'd
changed into a kangaroo. They were both absolutely

barmy, of course, but as Carla bounced away into the sunset with her beloved Ashton in the pouch, who amongst those watching could condemn the folly of it? The day would dawn, naturally, when they would both be certified; but, for that gobbet of time, their love was theirs alone. Let us leave it at that.

Even Red Butler was visibly moved as he watched his wife hop over the horizon. A burly policeman touched Butler on the shoulder and boomed sympathetically; 'We can bring them back, sir, and put them in the funny farm.'

Red Butler shook his head. 'No, officer,' he whispered. 'Leave them be. Who knows what will happen? After all, tomorrow is another day.' The policeman looked puzzled and asked, 'What does that mean?'

Butler shrugged his shoulders. 'I don't really know,' he replied. 'I read it somewhere.'

EPILOGUE

So ended the most dramatic episode in Britain's long and turbulent history. The nation would never be the same and many lives had been changed for ever.

The North and South conflict would leave scars that perhaps would never heal with time; there would be those whose hearts would never forgive the indignities of the Civil War, and Manchester City looked as if they'd never get out of the Fourth Division. For Red Butler, the future held promise of a knighthood and ten per cent off the price of an airline ticket with DanAir.

Melanie and her child were under contract with a agent in Paris and he'd got them a job yodelling in a wine-bar in Romania. Mr O'Mara was still living in his garden box and chewing lawns, but the neighbours wouldn't let him practise on his second-hand ukelele; in retaliation the old boy has started gnawing through car tyres. As for Carla and Ashton – well, up to the time of penning this saga (which I hope will sell enough to cover any alimony costs I may incur), they had not been hauled off for treatment, and she was spotted hopping somewhere in the New Forest with a pouch full of Ashton Whelks. As the man who had reported the sighting suffered from a drink problem, the report was discounted when the man threw up in a detective's pocket.

When the soft blur of dusk falls across the land, I often smoke my blackened briar and think perhaps it would be better if I smoked tobacco instead. And I try to imagine the passion of Ashton and Carla as they bounce into the history of this, our noble island. If I am ever blessed with grandchildren, I can say to them truthfully, 'I was there when it happened.'